The 1981 Charlton Coin Guide

21st Edition

**Dealers' Buying Prices For
Canadian, Newfoundland & Maritime Coinage
Canadian Medals, Tokens & Paper Money
United States & English Coinage**

The Charlton Press

The Charlton Press

299 Queen Street West,
Toronto, Ontario.
M5V 1Z9
Canada

(c) Copyright 1980 Charlton International Inc.
All Rights Reserved

ISSN 0706-0459
ISBN 0-88968-008-6

CONTENTS

INTRODUCTION

Can you identify valuable coins and banknotes that you might own? Do you know the value of the pieces you do own? This book contains all the essential information you need for buying and selling Canadian numismatic items. In simple and easy to read listings the current average prices are provided for Canadian coins, tokens, medals and paper money, and for coins of Great Britain and the United States.

This book is intended for everyone who wishes to identify and establish the value of his pieces. It is important that any owner or collector of currencies knows the facts. The secret to finding the value of what you own is in knowing what to look for. A careful reading of this book will help you understand the importance of an item's condition, familiarize you with rare dates, and help you identify and locate mint marks, signatures and other features that can affect value.

If you are considering money collecting as a hobby, then The Charlton Coin Guide will prove an invaluable basic handbook. As you read the book it will become apparent that it is not just a coin's or banknote's age that makes it valuable. Age, like scarcity and condition, is only one determining factor. Another, more subtle factor is the appeal of a numismatic item to collectors. An attractive design, a significant date in history, a slight variation in the pattern, may all cause a piece to be worth much more than its mintage figure or denomination would suggest.

There are many interesting and satisfying aspects to collecting, and it can be as inexpensive or expensive as you wish to make it. Whatever path you choose, you can't afford to be without The Charlton Coin Guide.

COINS OF CANADA

Introduction

Coin collecting has always attracted a certain following in Canada, but in terms of both interest and numbers of collectors, recent years have clearly seen the hobby reach an all-time high.

For the beginning collector, current coins can easily be obtained from pocket change or by examining rolls of coins obtained from banks. It is more difficult to obtain old coins in circulation, much more so that it was even ten years ago. For the most part silver no longer circulates since its bullion value now exceeds its face value. Generally speaking, the only pre-1968 coins in circulation are one-cent and five-cent pieces, and these seldon pre-date 1953. Older coins must now be purchased through dealers.

GRADING

Grading is the determination of the condition of a coin. In view of the high premiums paid for extremely fine and uncirculated coins, it is important that all collectors know at least the fundamentals of grading.

There have been many attempts to accurately describe each of the generally recognized grades, including, recently, a numerical system devised by the American Numismatic Association. Familiarity with the terminology and use of a grading guide will allow the collector to recognize overgraded coins, and prevent him from overgrading himself. Overgrading is simply describing a coin as being in better condition that it actually is. It can result from a number of causes — some obvious and others not so obvious. Whether it be inexperience, bargain hunting, eyestrain, greed, or some other reason, overgrading is a constant problem.

The following is a basic list and description of the most common grades of coins. More comprehensive descriptions and an illustrated grading outline are available in The Charlton Standard Catalogue of Canadian Coins for those wishing more detailed information.

MS-65: Brilliant Mint State or Uncirculated. In new condition with original mint lustre.

MS-60: Uncirculated. In new condition. Older coins may be dark from oxidation.

1

AU-50: About Uncirculated. With traces of wear on nearly all the high points, but at least half of the original mint lustre present.

EF-40: Extremely Fine. Little circulated with only slight evidence of wear.

VF-20: Very Fine. Moderate wear on higher parts of design.

F-12: Fine. More wear on higher parts than in Very Fine.

VG-8: Very Good. Much wear, but main features of design and legend are clear.

G-4: Good. Portrait, inscription, dates, considerably worn but legible.

Poor: Badly worn or mutilated, can contain holes, scratches or edge nicks. Listed prices are not paid for coins in this condition.

Grading should be done under reasonably constant magnification and illumination. Magnification should be either eight or four power, and the light source should be a 100 watt incandescent bulb at three feet.

SPECIMENS

Specimen, Proof, and Proof-like do not refer to a grade of condition but to a manner of production. In addition to the business strikes, or normal issue of coins, the mint also makes special issues. These coins are produced from polished blanks on different presses than business strikes. They are struck at slower speeds and higher pressures with special dies.

A Specimen striking produces a coin of distinctly higher quality. This is a coin not intended for circulation. The planchets are polished, as are the die faces, and this produces fine detail and a high lustre on the surface of the coin. Initially, Specimens were struck for special occasions, such as the opening of the mint in 1908, or the coronation of George V in 1911. Later, the mint produced Specimens for purchase by collectors.

For a number of years there has been some confusion over the meaning of the term Proof. Proof refers to a coin of the highest quality. By virtue of the production method, a Proof coin is also a type of Specimen. However, the quality of the finish on the coin is superior to the usual high quality of a Specimen coin. The criteria which the mint uses are those of the Royal Mint in England and not those of the mints in the United States. As far as the mint is concerned it did not produce a coin of Proof quality until the first issue of Olympic coins in 1973. Until then the mint did not possess the technology to produce a coin of British Proof standard.

About 1953 J.E. Charlton originated the term Proof-like to describe choice quality coins which were obviously superior to circulation strikes, but whose surfaces were not as bright as those of other collectors' coins (Specimens). Proof-like is not an official mint term. The mint prefers "uncirculated set." Although the mint refers to these coins as "uncirculated" they are not, as was believed, business strikes. They are struck on different presses, most often from selected planchets, and the chosen dies are usually the best which are available.

HANDLING AND CLEANING

Coins should be handled by the edges only. Avoid touching the surfaces. Many collectors have found too late that fingerprints cannot be removed from coins or other metal valuables. Proof and Specimen quality coins must be handled with extra care since their high lustre is very fragile.

Inevitably, the question of whether to clean coins or not will arise. Probably the best course to follow is, when in doubt — don't, until you have contacted an experienced collector or dealer. In the meantime, a wash in soap and water will remove most, if not all of the dirt. Wiping the coin with a soft towel after rinsing will provide sufficient rubbing action. It is not wise to use a brush, especially when cleaning gold coins.

Experts should be consulted if soap and water are not enough. The tarnish on silver coins can be removed, but it will not necessarily raise the value. If the tarnish is very thick, then its removal could leave the coin looking much worse. Only an experienced person can tell if the tarnish can be removed safely. If the removal of tarnish is possible, then the simplest method is to immerse the coin in a strong solution of baking soda and warm water in an aluminum pan. The tarnish will disappear, and the coin can then be rinsed in plain water and allowed to dry. The use of a silver "dip" is another method to remove tarnish. The coin should be dipped into the solution, rinsed in cool water (never hot), washed with soap, rinsed again, and allowed to dry. The soap neutralizes the remaining traces of the dip and retards tarnishing.

Nickel coins seldom require cleaning, and only soap and water are safe since nickel is a fairly active metal. Copper and bronze should not be cleaned by anyone who is not knowledgeable in the chemical properties of these metals and their alloys.

Whatever the metal, abrasives must never be used. There are many polishes on the market which are designed for silverware, copper and brass. These must not be used with coins. The results are disasterous.

BUYING AND SELLING PRICES

Buying prices are what dealers pay for coins. Selling prices are what dealers charge for coins. Generally, dealers will pay 40% to 60% of their selling price. It should be remembered, all dealers will pay according to their needs. They will pay well for what they need immediately, but for those coins for which there is no demand, even if they have a high retail value, they will offer substantially less. Of the current coins in circulation only the nickel coins of 1970, the 1973 Large Bust 25-cent piece, the 1977 dollar and 50-cent pieces, and a few rare variants have any significant premium.

The prices shown in this book represent averages or estimates of buying prices, and should serve as a guide in negotiating fair prices when buying or selling. Also a clearer idea of what coins are in demand by collectors and dealers can be developed by studying the guide.

Coins should not be mailed for appraisal unless a written response to an inquiry is received from the dealer. If coins are mailed, then they should be sent by registered mail, insured, accompanied by a list of the coins sent, and with a complete return address and return postage.

GENUINE OR FAKE?

Currently, coin collecting is cursed with counterfeits of important dates and varieties. Since 1970 many well-known pieces have been counterfeited. First it was the $20 gold pieces of 1967, then the $5 and $10 pieces of 1912-1914. More recently it has been the rarer silver dollars, and some of the Olympic coins. Counterfeit issues of the 5- and 50-cent pieces of 1921, and the dot 1- and 10-cent pieces of 1936 are well known, but they can deceive the unwary or inexperienced collector even today. Before buying, be sure that what you are looking at is genuine. Beware of "bargains." When confronted with a bargain, ask why the coin is being offered so cheaply. The coin might be overgraded, stolen, or counterfeit. The detection of imitations can be difficult at times, and every serious collector should attend at least one seminar on this topic. Seminars are available at many coin shows.

MINT MARKS

A mint mark is a letter stamped on a coin to designate the mint that produced the coins.

Canadian decimal coinage issued prior to 1908 was struck at either the Tower Mint, London, in which case it had no mint mark, or at the Heaton Mint in Birmingham. The Birmingham coins had a small "H" as a mint mark. Since 1908 all Canadian coins have been struck at Ottawa with no mint marks, except the Canadian sovereigns which were identified by a small "C" above the date.

Newfoundland's coinage was struck at either London, Birmingham, or Ottawa. The Tower Mint coins had no mark, the Birmingham coins had an "H", and the Ottawa coins had a "C", except for the 1940 and 1942 cent pieces.

New Brunswick's and Nova Scotia's coinage had no mint marks because it was struck at the Tower Mint.

Prince Edward Island's coinage was struck at Birmingham but no mint mark was used because the dies were supplied by the Tower Mint.

ARTISTS MARKS
(Canadian Coins)

B.M.	Sir Bertram MacKennal
P.M.	Percy Metcalfe
D.E.S.	G.W. DeSaulles
D.V.	Dinko Vodanovic
E.H.	Emmanuel Hahn
H.P.	Humphrey Paget
K.G.	Kruger-Gray
L.C.W. or L.W.	Leonard C. Wyon
P.C.	Paul Cedarberg
M.G.	Mrs. Mary Gillick
P.P.	Paul Pederson
D.D.P.	Donald D. Paterson
R.T.	Raymond Taylor
T.M.	Terry Manning
S.T.	Stephan Trenka
T.S.	Thomas Shingles
W.W.	William Wyon
P.B.	Patrick Brindley

Nova Scotia

Nova Scotia adopted the decimal system in 1859. In the Nova Scotia system the pound sterling was worth $5, which allowed for the use of English silver. However, it was still necessary to mint a half-cent piece in order to make change for the sixpence, which was worth 12½ cents. The half-cent piece was equal in size and weight to the British farthing. It weighed 2.84 grams or 160 to the pound avoirdupois.

The cent was equal in size and weight to the Province of Canada large cent and the British halfpenny. In 1861 there were two varieties of the cent. To the right of "SCOTIA," Type 1 showed a large rosebud, and Type 2 a smaller one. All the cents of 1862 and 1864 had the smaller rosebud. The obverse design was by L.C. Wyon, and the reverse design by J.C. Hill.

VICTORIA 1861 - 1864

Date and Denomination	Mintage (1,000's)	Buying Price
1861 ½ cent	400	2.00
1864 ½ cent	400	2.00
1861 1 cent	800	.40
1862 1 cent	100	5.00
1864 1 cent	800	.40

New Brunswick

New Brunswick adopted the decimal system in 1860. Under the mistaken belief that the New Brunswick standard was the same as the Nova Scotia standard a minting error was made. A half-cent piece was minted which was not needed since the New Brunswick standard was the Canadian dollar. The unneeded coins were returned to England for melting, but some were inadvertently mixed with a shipment of half-cent pieces for Nova Scotia, and they ended up in circulation.

Except for the name, the New Brunswick cent and half-cent pieces were of the same design as the Nova Scotia pieces.

The silver coins of New Brunswick closely resemble those issued for Canada in 1858, and they were also designed by L.C. Wyon. The 5-cent piece weighed 1.162 grams, the 10-cent piece weighed 2.324 grams, and the 20-cent piece weighed 4.648 grams.

VICTORIA 1861 - 1864

Date and Denomination	Mintage (1,000's)	Buying Price
1861 ½ cent	222	25.00
1861 1 cent	1,000	.40
1864 1 cent	1,000	.40
1862 5 cents	100	15.00
1864 5 cents	100	15.00
1862 10 cents	150	10.00
1864 10 cents	100	10.00
1862 20 cents	150	6.00
1864 20 cents	150	6.00

Prince Edward Island

Prince Edward Island adopted the decimal system in 1871, and the only issue was the cent of that year. Coined in bronze, this issue was the only coin in British North America to ever carry the Royal titles in English. The obverse carried a diademed portrait of Victoria adapted from an 1866 bust by William Theed. The reverse bore an adaption by L.C. Wyon of the colony's seal.

VICTORIA 1871

Date and Denomination	Mintage (1,000's)	Buying Price
1871 1 cent	2,000	.25

Newfoundland

LARGE CENTS

VICTORIA: Newfoundland adopted the decimal system in 1863 and issued its first coins in 1865. The Victorian cent bears the laureate bust by L.C. Wyon which was also found on the Nova Scotia and New Brunswick cents. The reverse was designed by Horace Morehan and engraved by T.J. Minton.

Round 0   Oval 0

VICTORIA 1865 - 1896

Date and Mint Mark	Mintage (1,000's)	Buying Price
1865	240	.50
1872H	200	.50
1873	200	.50
1876H	200	.50
1880 Round 0	400	.50
1880 Oval 0	Incl.	25.00
1885	40	6.00
1888	50	5.00
1890	200	.50
1894	200	.50
1896	200	.50

EDWARD VII: The G.W. DeSaulles obverse depicted a crowned, robed bust of the King, with the chain of The Order of the Garter fastened at the shoulder. The reverse was similar to the Victorian issue, except the St. Edward's crown was replaced with the Imperial crown.

EDWARD VII 1904 - 1909

Date and Mint Mark	Mintage (1,000's)	Buying Price
1904H	100	2.00
1907	200	.60
1909	200	.60

GEORGE V: The bust on the obverse was designed by Sir Bertram MacKennal. It was combined with the Blakemore reverse used for the Edward VII series. The cents of 1917, 1919, and 1920 carried a letter "C" over the "UN" of "NEWFOUNDLAND."

GEORGE V 1913 - 1936

Date and Mint Mark	Mintage (1,000's)	Buying Price
1913	400	.20
1917C	702	.20
1919C	300	.20
1920C	302	.20
1929	300	.20
1936	300	.20

10

SMALL CENTS

GEORGE VI: In 1938 the Newfoundland cent was reduced in size. It was minted at 3.24 grams or 140 to the pound avoirdupois, the same specifications as the Canadian small cent. The reverse design of a pitcher plant, a plant native to Newfoundland, was adapted for the coins by Walter Newman from a drawing submitted by the government. The obverse bore a bust of the King by Percy Metcalfe.

The issues from 1940 to 1947 were coined at the Royal Canadian Mint in Ottawa. All the issues were marked by a small "C" to the right of the date except for accidental omissions in 1940 and 1942.

GEORGE VI 1938 - 1948

Date and Mint Mark	Mintage (1,000's)	Buying Price
1938	500	.10
1940	300	.65
1941C	827	.05
1942	1,996	.05
1943C	1,239	.05
1944C	1,328	.20
1947C	313	.10

FIVE CENTS

VICTORIA: The Newfoundland five-cent piece in sterling silver was first coined in 1865 at a weight of 1.178 grams. The weight was lowered to 1.166 grams in 1917. In 1945 the silver fineness was reduced to .800. The 1873H five-cent piece is very rare and collectors should be wary of counterfeits.

VICTORIA 1865 - 1896

Date and Mint Mark	Mintage (1,000's)	Buying Price
1865	80	8.00
1870	40	9.00
1872H	40	8.00
1873	44	9.00
1873H	Incl.	135.00
1876H	20	15.00
1880	40	9.00
1881	40	5.00
1882H	60	4.00
1885	16	30.00
1888	40	5.00
1890	160	1.50
1894	160	1.50
1896	400	1.25

EDWARD VII, GEORGE V, and GEORGE VI: The Edward VII five-cent piece was designed by DeSaulles, and its reverse was also used for both George V and George VI issues. The obverses for these later series were designed by MacKennal and Metcalfe, respectively.

EDWARD VII 1903 - 1908

Date and Mint Mark	Mintage (1,000's)	Buying Price
1903	100	.75
1904H	100	.75
1908	400	.50

GEORGE V 1912 - 1929

Date and Mint Mark	Mintage (1,000's)	Buying Price
1912	300	.50
1917C	300	.50
1919C	100	.75
1929	300	.50

GEORGE VI 1938 - 1947

Date and Mint Mark	Mintage (1,000's)	Buying Price
1938	100	.50
1940C	200	.50
1941C	612	.50
1942C	298	.50
1943C	351	.50
1944C	286	.50
1945C	203	.50
1946C	2	100.00
1947C	38	1.00

TEN CENTS

Newfoundland's sterling silver ten-cent pieces were first coined in 1865. They were minted initially with a weight of 2.356 grams, but this was reduced to 2.333 grams in 1917. In 1945 the fineness was reduced to .800. In each reign the designs were kept the same as the five-cent piece designs. Only the value numbers were altered.

VICTORIA 1865 - 1896

Date and Mint Mark	Mintage (1,000's)	Buying Price
1865	80	4.00
1870	30	45.00
1872H	40	3.00
1873	23	4.50
1876H	10	9.00
1880	10	9.00
1882H	20	3.00
1885	8	14.00
1888	30	3.50
1890	100	1.25
1894	100	1.25
1896	230	1.00

EDWARD VII 1903 - 1904

Date and Mint Mark	Mintage (1,000's)	Buying Price
1903	100	1.00
1904H	100	1.00

GEORGE V 1912 - 1919

Date and Mint Mark	Mintage (1,000's)	Buying Price
1912	150	1.00
1917C	250	1.00
1919C	54	1.00

GEORGE VI 1938 - 1947

Date and Mint Mark	Mintage (1,000's)	Buying Price
1938	100	1.00
1940	100	1.00
1941C	483	1.00
1942C	292	1.00
1943C	104	1.00
1944C	151	1.00
1945C	175	1.00
1946C	38	2.00
1947C	61	1.00

TWENTY CENTS

The first 20-cent pieces, or fifths as they were also called, were coined in 1865. Minted in sterling silver with a weight of 4.713 grams, they carried the same designs as the five- and ten-cent pieces, except the value number was changed accordingly. In the course of time some of these coins found their way into circulation in Eastern Canada, and were defaced so they could be passed off as 25-cent pieces. These defaced coins are worth only their bullion value, regardless of their date.

VICTORIA 1865 - 1900

Date and Mint Mark	Mintage (1,000's)	Buying Price
1865	100	2.25
1870	50	3.00
1872H	90	2.00
1873	45	2.50
1876H	50	3.25
1880	30	3.25
1881	60	2.00
1882H	100	2.00
1885	40	2.00
1888	75	2.00
1890	100	2.00
1894	100	2.00
1896	125	2.00
1899	125	2.00
1900	125	2.00

EDWARD VII 1904

Date and Mint Mark	Mintage (1,000's)	Buying Price
1904H	75	2.50

GEORGE V 1912

Date	Mintage (1,000's)	Buying Price
1912	350	2.00

TWENTY-FIVE CENTS

The Newfoundland 25-cent pieces were introduced in 1917 at
the suggestion of the Ottawa mint. The 20-cent piece, which was
similar in size to the Canadian 25-cent piece, was being confused
at the mint with the Canadian piece. The Newfoundland 25-cent
piece was coined in 1917 and 1919 in sterling silver with a weight
of 5.832 grams. The MacKennal portrait of George V was used
on the obverse, and the reverse was by W.H.J. Blakemore.

GEORGE V 1917 - 1919

Date and Mint Mark	Mintage (1,000's)	Buying Price
1917C	464	2.50
1919C	163	2.50

FIFTY CENTS

The Newfoundland 50-cent piece was introduced in 1870. It
was coined in sterling silver and weighed 11.782 grams. In 1917
the weight was lowered to 11.664 grams. Except for the value
number, the design features were the same as those of the other
coins minted for that year.

The reverses of the 1870 to 1880 coins showed a cartouche
with thick loops. From 1881 to 1900 the cartouche had thinner
and smaller loops. The 50-cent pieces of 1891 were struck with

either a large or a small date. The 1899 issue had either wide or narrow 9's in the date, the wide 9's had an almost circular loop.

VICTORIA 1870 - 1900

Date and Mint Mark	Mintage (1,000's)	Buying Price
1870	50	5.00
1872H	48	5.00
1873	37	5.00
1874	80	5.00
1876H	28	7.50
1880	24	7.50
1881	60	5.00
1882H	100	5.00
1885	40	5.00
1888	20	6.00
1894	40	5.00
1896	60	5.00
1898	79	5.00
1899	150	5.00
1900	150	5.00

EDWARD VII 1904 - 1909

Date and Mint Mark	Mintage (1,000's)	Buying Price
1904H	140	5.00
1907	100	5.00
1908	160	5.00
1909	200	5.00

GEORGE V 1911 - 1919

Date and Mint Mark	Mintage (1,000's)	Buying Price
1911	200	5.00
1917C	375	5.00
1918C	294	5.00
1919C	306	5.00

GOLD COINS

Newfoundland's gold $2 piece was issued intermittently from 1865 to 1888 in 22k gold and at 3.328 grams. The obverse used L.C. Wyon's laureate bust of Victoria. The reverse, also by Wyon, bore the value expressed in dollars, cents, and pence. All dates are scarce and the coinage from 1880 is rare. Buyer's should be aware of possible counterfeits.

Two Dollars

VICTORIA 1865 - 1888

Date and Mint Mark	Mintage (1,000's)	Buying Price (V.F.)
1865	10	175.00
1870	10	175.00
1872	6	250.00
1880	2	700.00
1881	10	175.00
1882H	25	175.00
1885	10	175.00
1888	25	175.00

Province of Canada

LARGE CENTS

Canada adopted the decimal system in 1858 and the first issue of coinage occurred later in that year. The initial issue of coins was so large (there were 10,000,000 one-cent pieces) that no new coins were minted for a number of years. The Victorian cents, like all Victorian coinage, was designed by L.C. Wyon of the Royal Mint in London.

VICTORIA: In the 1859 issue of the one-cent piece a number of date varieties appeared. Both wide and narrow 9's were used, the wide 9 showed a circular loop and the narrow 9 a more oval one. It is important that a true wide 9 be distinguished from a 9 widened by wear. There were also two types of overpunched 9's. Type 1 had a small fragment missing from the lower front of the 9. Type 2 had an imperfect alignment on the overpunch and this produced a trace of the first impression to the left.

Laurel Wreath
Head
1858 - 1859

VICTORIA 1858-1859

Date	Mintage (1,000's)	Buying Price
1858	421	20.00
1859	9,579	.50

FIVE CENTS

The five-cent piece chosen by the Province of Canada was a small silver coin, similar to the United States half dime. The design and engraving was done by L.C. Wyon.

VICTORIA: The first dies of the 1858 issue bore small, widely spaced digits in the date. Later strikings carried larger digits punched over the original small figures.

Small Date   Large Date

VICTORIA 1858

Date	Mintage (1,000's)	Buying Price
1858 Small Date	1,460	5.00
1858 Large Date	Incl.	50.00

TEN CENTS

VICTORIA: In design, the Province of Canada ten-cent piece resembles the five-cent piece. It was struck in sterling silver and weighed 2.32 grams.

VICTORIA 1858

Date	Mintage (1,000's)	Buying Price
1858	1,216	4.00

TWENTY CENTS

VICTORIA: The 20-cent piece was issued only in 1858 and it was never very popular. It was designed by L.C. Wyon and struck in sterling silver weighing 4.65 grams. These coins, which were continually confused with 25-cent pieces, were systematically withdrawn from circulation after Confederation. Between 1885 and 1906 more than half of the original issue was withdrawn.

VICTORIA 1858

Date	Mintage (1,000's)	Buying Price
1858 Single Year Issue	730	25.00

Dominion of Canada

LARGE CENTS

VICTORIA: The Dominion of Canada government initially used what was left of the enormous production of 1858-1859 Province of Canada large cents. The first cents struck for the Dominion came out in 1876.

In the 1891 issue there were large and small date varieties. The large date variety, which also had large leaves in the reverse design, showed a more nearly circular loop on the "9" than the "9" in the small date variety did. The small date variety usually had a reverse pattern with small leaves, but some of the issue was struck with the large leaves reverse.

Part of the 1900 striking was done at the Heaton Mint in Birmingham, England. It was distinguished by the small "H" stamped at the bottom of the reverse. There is a considerable price difference between these two varieties.

Tiara Head
1876 - 1901

Large Date, Large Leaves

Small Date, Small Leaves

Note the location of "H" mint mark. On the other large cents it appears under the date.

Date and Mint Mark	Mintage (1,000's)	Buying Price
1876H	4,000	.50
1881H	2,000	.75
1882H	4,000	.50
1884	2,500	.50
1886	1,500	.75
1887	1,500	.75
1888	4,000	.50
1890H	1,000	2.00
1891 Large Date	1,452	2.00
1891 Small Date	Incl.	17.50
1892	1,200	.75
1893	2,000	.50
1894	1,000	2.00
1895	1,200	.80
1896	2,000	.50
1897	1,500	.50
1898H	1,000	1.50
1899	2,400	.50
1900	1,000	2.00
1900H	2,600	.50
1901	4,100	.50

Large Cents were not issued for the years omitted in this listing.

EDWARD VII: The design was by G.W. DeSaulles. The coins were the same size and weight as the 1876 cents, the second Victorian issue of this denomination. They were 1 inch in diameter and 80 to the pound avoirdupois. The 1858-1859 issue of cents was the same diameter but lighter: 100 to the pound.

Note that there is a substantial price difference for the 1907 and 1907H cents.

EDWARD VII 1902 - 1910

Date and Mint Mark	Mintage (1,000's)	Buying Price
1902	3,000	.35
1903	4,000	.35
1904	2,500	.40
1905	2,000	.60
1906	4,100	.40
1907	2,400	.40
1907H	800	4.00
1908	2,401	.40
1909	3,973	.35
1910	5,146	.35

GEORGE V: The design for the reverse was by W.H.J. Blakemore, and for the obverse by Sir Bertram MacKennal.

The 1911 cent, like all 1911 Canadian coins, had "DEI GRATIA" (By the Grace of God) removed from the Royal titles. The coins of this year were called "Godless" or "Godless and Graceless." The latin phrase was reinstituted for the 1912 and all succeeding issues of coinage.

GEORGE V 1911 - 1920

Date	Mintage (1,000's)	Buying Price
1911	4,663	.25
1912	5,108	.20
1913	5,735	.20
1914	3,406	.30
1915	4,932	.20
1916	11,022	.15
1917	11,899	.15
1918	12,971	.15
1919	11,280	.15
1920	6,762	.15

SMALL CENTS

GEORGE V: Introduced in 1920, the small cent was considerably lighter: 3.24 grams or 140 to the pound avoirdupois. A new reverse was designed by a Canadian Mint employee, Fred Lewis.

GEORGE V 1920 - 1936

Date	Mintage (1,000's)	Buying Price
1920	15,484	.05
1921	7,602	.10
1922	1,244	5.00
1923	1,019	10.00
1924	1,593	2.50
1925	1,001	8.00
1926	2,143	1.00
1927	3,554	.50
1928	9,145	.04
1929	12,160	.04
1930	2,539	.75
1931	3,843	.30
1932	21,316	.03
1933	12,079	.03
1934	7,042	.03
1935	7,526	.03
1936	8,769	.03

GEORGE VI: The obverse was designed by T.H. Paget, and the reverse by G. Kruger-Gray. In 1947 India was granted independence and the use of the King's title, Emperor of India, "ET IND:IMP" in Latin abbreviation, was discontinued. To meet demand until the new dies arrived in 1948 an extra issue of coins was struck with a 1947 date. This issue was identified by the small maple leaf after the date.

Date	Mintage (1,000's)	Buying Price
1937	10,040	.03
1938	18,366	.01
1939	21,600	.01
1940	85,741	.01
1941	56,336	.01
1942	76,114	.01
1943	89,112	.01
1944	44,131	.01
1945	77,270	.01
1946	56,662	.01
1947	31,094	.01
1947 Maple Leaf	43,855	.01

In 1948, "ET IND:IMP." ceased to appear on the coinage.

Date	Mintage (1,000's)	Buying Price
1948	25,768	.01
1949	33,129	.01
1950	60,445	.01
1951	80,430	.01
1952	67,632	.01

ELIZABETH II: The initial obverse design by Mary Gillick was combined with the earlier Kruger-Gray reverse. The original strikings of 1953 did not provide good details on the obverse. The relief was lowered at the Ottawa mint by Thomas Shingles. The details of the Queen's gown were cut more deeply, producing the "Shoulder Fold" variety.

No Shoulder Fold   Shoulder Fold

ELIZABETH II 1953 to date

Date	Mintage (1,000's)	Buying Price
1953 No Shoulder Fold	67,806	.01
1953 Shoulder Fold	Incl.	.25
1954	22,182	.01
1955	56,403	.01
1956	78,686	.01
1957	100,602	.01
1958	59,386	.01
1959	83,615	.01
1960	75,773	.01
1961	139,598	.01
1962	227,244	.01
1963	279,076	.01
1964	484,655	.01

In 1965 a new obverse known as the "Mature Bust" was designed by Arnold Machin and in 1979 a smaller, re-engraved bust was introduced. The reverse remained the same for all issues except the Centennial coinage. New reverses were designed for all 1967 denominations by Alex Colville.

The issues of 1965 had a number of date and head size varieties and this can change the value of individual coins.

Centennial Reverse by Nova Scotia artist
Alex Colville.

Date	Mintage (1,000's)	Buying Price
1965	304,441	.01
1966	183,644	.01
1967 Dove	345,141	.01
1968	329,696	.01
1969	335,241	.01
1970	311,145	.01
1971	298,229	.01
1972	451,305	.01
1973	457,060	.01
1974	692,058	.01
1975	642,318	.01
1976	701,123	.01
1977	453,051	.01
1978	911,171	.01
1979	753,943	.01
1980	N/A	.01

FIVE CENTS

The first five-cent pieces for the Dominion of Canada were
introduced in 1870. The initial designs were identical to those
used for the Province of Canada in 1858. Minted in sterling
silver, the 1858 coins weighed 1.162 grams. The weight was
increased to 1.166 grams in 1908. In 1920 the fineness was
reduced to .800. Five-cent pieces have been struck in nickel,
steel, and a brass alloy called tombac. Nickel, which has been
used exclusively since 1955, was first used for the 1922-1942
issues. It was used also for the 1946-1950 issues, and the 1951
commemorative issue. Steel was first used in 1944-1945 and
again in 1951. Tombac was used only for most of the 1942 and all
of the 1943 issues.

VICTORIA: In the 1870 issue there were wide and narrow rim varieties. The more unusual wide rim also has unusually long rim denticles.

In 1874 and 1875 two sizes of digits were used for dating the dies. In addition the two date sizes for 1874 also differ in the style of the "4": the small date contains a plain "4" and the large date contains a crosslet "4".

Two sizes of dates are also seen on the 1900 issue. The 1900 Large Date has wide "0's" and "9's", the Small Date, narrow ones.

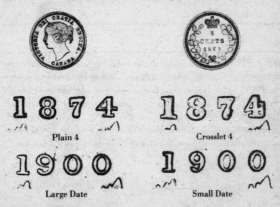

Plain 4   Crosslet 4

Large Date   Small Date

VICTORIA 1870 - 1901

Date and Mint Mark	Mintage (1,000's)	Buying Price
1870	2,800	3.00
1871	1,400	3.00
1872H	2,000	2.25
1874H Plain 4	800	5.50
1874H Crosslet 4	Incl.	3.00
1875H	1,000	25.00
1880H	3,000	1.50
1881H	1,500	2.00
1882H	1,000	1.50
1883H	600	3.50
1884	200	25.00
1885	1,000	2.00
1886	1,700	1.25
1887	500	3.50
1888	1,000	1.25
1889	1,200	6.00
1890H	1,000	1.10

Date and Mint Mark	Mintage (1,000's)	Buying Price
1891	1,800	1.10
1892	860	1.65
1893	1,700	1.10
1894	500	4.25
1896	1,500	1.10
1897	1,319	1.10
1898	581	2.50
1899	3,000	1.10
1900 Large Date	1,800	1.00
1900 Small Date	Incl.	3.75
1901	2,000	1.00

EDWARD VII: The basic design was by G.W. DeSaulles. In the 1903 issue the St. Edward's crown used in the reverse design was changed to the Imperial crown. This made the reverse design consistent with all other denominations of the Edward issues. Two sizes of "H" appear on the 1902 Heaton issue of this denomination. The wreath on the reverse of the 1903H coin had 21 leaves, while that on the plain 1903 coin had 22 leaves.

 Small H

 Large H

EDWARD VII 1902 - 1910

Date and Mint Mark	Mintage (1,000's)	Buying Price
1902	2,120	.50
1902 Large H	2,200	.50
1902 Small H	Incl.	3.50
1903	1,000	1.25
1903H	2,640	.70
1904	2,400	.75
1905	2,600	.70
1906	3,100	.65
1907	5,200	.50
1908	1,221	1.50
1909	1,984	.75
1910	5,580	.50

GEORGE V: The use of the DeSaulles reverse continued, and it was combined with an obverse designed by Sir Bertram MacKennal.

For information on the 1911 issue see the one-cent section.

GEORGE V 1911 - 1921

Date	Mintage (1,000's)	Buying Price
1911	3,692	.75
1912	5.863	.50
1913	5.588	.50
1914	4,202	.50
1915	1,172	2.50
1916	2,482	.70
1917	5,521	.50
1918	6,052	.50
1919	7,835	.50
1920	10,650	.50

The 1921 issue is extremely valuable and only a few hundred specimens are known. Beware of counterfeits. Most of the 1921 strike was melted down when the mint shifted to nickel composition in 1922.

Date	Mintage (1,000's)	Buying Price
1921	2,582*	750.00

*Majority melted down, approximately 200 known.

The nickel issue of 1922 was similar in size and weight to the American five-cent piece, the weight being 4.54 grams or 100 to the pound avoirdupois. The new reverse was designed by Fred Lewis.

GEORGE V 1922 - 1936

Date	Mintage (1,000's)	Buying Price
1922	4,794	.07
1923	2,502	.10
1924	3,106	.07
1925	202	17.50

In the Near "6" variety of the 1926 issue, the top of the figure "6" nearly touches the maple leaf, in the Far "6" variety it is farther away. Beware of altered "6" on the Far "6" variety. Base of the figure "2" is in line with the base of the figure "6" on genuine Far "6" variety.

Near 6   Far 6

Date	Mintage (1,000's)	Buying Price
1926 Near 6	983	1.50
1926 Far 6	Incl.	50.00
1927	5,286	.07
1928	4,578	.07
1929	5,612	.07
1930	3,705	.07
1931	5,100	.07
1932	3,199	.07
1933	2,598	.07
1934	3,827	.07
1935	3,900	.07
1936	4,400	.07

GEORGE VI: The 1937 obverse design was by T.H. Paget and the reverse was by G. Kruger-Gray. The dot after the 1937 date was intended as a design feature only.

In 1943 a new reverse by T. Shingles shows a V and torch design and instead of the usual border beads there was a Morse Code message: "We Win When We Work Willingly."

In 1944 a chrome-plated steel issue replaced the tombac, and collectors should be wary of steel issues which have been replated to appear as uncirculated.

The 1947 maple leaf five-cent piece was a 1948 emergency issue. For more information see the one-cent section.

GEORGE VI 1937 - 1952

Date		Mintage (1,000's)	Buying Price
1937	Dot	4,593	.05
1938		3,899	.05
1939		5,661	.05
1940		13,920	.05
1941		8,682	.05
1942	Nickel	6,848	.05
1942	Tombac Beaver	3,396	.15
1943	Tombac V	24,760	.10
1944		11,532	.05
1945		18,893	.05
1946		6,953	.05
1947	Maple Leaf	9,595	.05
1948		1,811	.25
1949		13,037	.05
1950		11,971	.05

In 1951 there was a nickel commemorative issue to celebrate the bicentennial of the isolation of nickel by the Swedish chemist A.F. Crondstedt. The reverse for this issue was designed by Stephan Trenka.

Nickel Commemorative

Steel 5¢ Piece

Date	Mintage (1,000's)	Buying Price
1951 Commemorative	9,029	.05
1951 Beaver	4,313	.05
1952	10,891	.05

ELIZABETH II: The initial 1953 obverse was by Mary Gillick. The beaver reverse was used. In 1965 the obverse was changed to Arnold Machin's diademed bust of the Queen, and this was redesigned for the 1979 coins. The only reverse change was for the Centennial coins.

Mature Bust

Centennial Reverse by Nova Scotia artist Alex Colville.

Date	Mintage (1,000's)	Buying Price
1953	16,636	.05
1954	6,999	.05
1955	5,355	.05
1956	9,400	.05
1957	7,388	.05
1958	7,608	.05
1959	11,553	.05
1960	37,157	.05
1961	47,889	.05
1962	46,307	.05
1963	43,970	.05
1964	78,075	.05
1965	84,876	.05
1966	27,678	.05
1967 Rabbit	36,877	.05
1968	99,253	.05
1969	27,830	.05
1970	5,726	.10
1971	27,313	.05
1972	62,417	.05
1973	53,507	.05
1974	94,705	.05
1975	138,882	.05
1976	55,140	.05
1977	89,121	.05
1978	137,079	.05
1979	186,296	.05
1980	N/A	.05

TEN CENTS

The initial designs for the Victoria ten-cent pieces issued by the Dominion government were identical to the 1858 Province of Canada issue. That coin was struck in sterling silver and weighed 2.324 grams. The weight was increased to 2.333 grams in 1908. In 1920 the fineness was reduced to .800 and in 1967 to .500. The ten-cent piece was first coined in nickel in 1968.

VICTORIA: The design and engraving was done by L.C. Wyon. Several minor changes occurred in the portrait. The wreath on the reverse had 21 leaves for the 1858 to 1881H strikings, and thereafter had 22 leaves.

VICTORIA 1870 - 1901

Date and Mint Mark	Mintage (1,000's)	Buying Price
1870	1,600	3.50
1871	800	4.00
1871H	1,870	6.50
1872H	1,000	35.00
1874H	600	3.00
1875H	1,000	60.00
1880H	1,500	2.50
1881H	950	3.50
1882H	1,000	2.50
1883H	300	6.00
1884	150	45.00
1885	400	4.00
1886	800	3.75
1887	350	4.00
1888	500	4.00
1889	600	135.00
1890H	450	3.50
1891	800	3.50
1892	520	3.00

The ten-cent piece of 1893 with a round-topped "3" is very rare. Counterfeits made by cutting open the left side of the final 8 of an 1898 ten-cent piece show a "3" of a different shape, on which the balls on the ends of the top and bottom curves are absent.

Flat Top 3

Round Top 3

Date	Mintage (1,000's)	Buying Price
1893 Flat Top 3	500	3.50
1893 Round Top 3	Incl.	200.00
1894	500	2.50
1896	650	2.00

Date	Mintage (1,000's)	Buying Price
1898	720	2.00
1899	1,200	1.50
1900	1,100	1.00
1901	1,200	1.00

EDWARD VII: The design was by G.W. DeSaulles, and was introduced in 1902. A modified reverse with broader leaves in the wreath, by W.H.J. Blakemore, was introduced in 1909. The cluster of leaves to the right of the crown is larger and on worn coins it appears as one large leaf.

EDWARD VII 1902 - 1910

Date and Mint Mark	Mintage (1,000's)	Buying Price
1902	720	1.00
1902H	1,100	1.00
1903	500	2.00
1903H	1,320	1.00
1904	1,000	2.00
1905	1,000	1.50
1906	1,700	1.00
1907	2,620	1.00
1908	777	1.00
1909	1,697	1.00
1910	4,468	1.00

GEORGE V: The coins of 1911 were "Godless." See the section on one-cent pieces for more information. The 1912 issue and a small part of the 1913 issue used the 1909 Blakemore reverse with large leaves. A new reverse with conspicuously smaller leaves in the wreath was used for most of 1913 and all ensuing issues.

| Broad Leaves | Small Leaves |

GEORGE V 1911 - 1936

Date		Mintage (1,000's)	Buying Price
1911		2,738	3.50
1912		3,236	1.00
1913	Broad Leaves	3,614	20.00
1913	Small Leaves	Incl.	1.00
1914		2,549	1.00
1915		688	1.00
1916		4,218	1.00
1917		5,011	1.00
1918		5,133	1.00
1919		7,877	1.00
1920		6,305	1.00
1921		2,469	1.00
1928		2,458	1.00
1929		3,253	1.00
1930		1,831	1.00
1931		2,067	1.00
1932		1,154	1.00
1933		672	1.00
1934		409	1.00
1935		384	1.00
1936		2,461	1.00

GEORGE VI: The coinage of George VI was introduced in 1937 with Paget's bust of the King and the schooner reverse by Emmanuel Hahn. The date on the 1937 coins was quite small. It proved to wear poorly and in 1938 the dates were enlarged and raised further above the water line.

For information on the 1947 Maple Leaf ten-cent piece see the one-cent section.

GEORGE VI 1937 - 1952

Date	Mintage (1,000's)	Buying Price
1937	2,500	1.00
1938	4,197	1.00
1939	5,502	1.00
1940	16,526	1.00
1941	8,716	1.00
1942	10,214	1.00
1943	21,143	1.00
1944	9,384	1.00
1945	10,980	1.00
1946	6,300	1.00
1947	4,431	.60
1947 Maple Leaf	9,639	1.00
1948	423	2.50
1949	11,336	1.00
1950	17,823	1.00
1951	15,079	1.00
1952	10,474	1.00

ELIZABETH II: The ten-cent pieces first released in 1953 used the laureate bust of the Queen by Mary Gillick, and continued the use of Hahn's schooner reverse. Later, the obverse was re-engraved by Thomas Shingles to produce the 1953 "Shoulder Fold" obverse. For more information see the one-cent section. In 1965 Arnold Machin's mature bust of the Queen with a diadem was introduced, and for the 1979 issue this was re-engraved. A Centennial reverse showing a mackerel by Alex Colville was used in 1967.

ELIZABETH II   1953 to date

Date	Mintage (1,000's)	Buying Price
1953	17,706	1.00
1954	4,493	1.00
1955	12,237	1.00
1956	16,733	1.00
1957	16,110	1.00
1958	10,621	1.00
1959	19,691	1.00
1960	45,447	1.00
1961	26,851	1.00
1962	41,864	1.00
1963	41,916	1.00
1964	49,519	1.00
1965	56,965	1.00
1966	34,330	1.00

The ten-cent pieces of 1967 were minted in either .800 fine or .500 fine silver. It became necessary late in 1967 to reduce the fineness because of an increase in the price of silver. In 1968 some coins were minted in silver before a complete shift was made to nickel. The nickel coins of 1968 were minted at either the Ottawa or the Philadelphia mints and the coins are distinguishable. The Ottawa coins have V grooves in the edge reeding and the Philadelphia coins have flat-bottom grooves.

Date	Mintage (1,000's)	Buying Price
1967 Mackeral, .800 Fine Silver	32,309	.75
1967 Mackerel, .500 Fine Silver	30,689	.75
1968 .500 Fine Silver	70,460	.50
1968 Nickel	172,583	.10

In 1969 the reverse was completely redesigned by Myron Cook. The new style showed a slightly smaller schooner with smaller lettering and date. A few ten-cent pieces were struck with the old reverse but only two such coins are known.

Small Date

Large Date

Date	Mintage (1,000's)	Buying Price
1969 Small Date	55,834	.10
1969 Large Date - RARE	Incl.	200.00
1970	5,249	.10
1971	41,016	.10
1972	60,269	.10
1973	167,715	.10
1974	201,566	.10
1975	207,680	.10
1976	95,018	.10
1977	128,452	.10
1978	170,394	.10
1979	236,910	.10
1980	N/A	.10

TWENTY-FIVE CENTS

The Canadian 25-cent piece was introduced in 1870 in sterling silver weighing 5.81 grams. The weight was increased to 5.83 grams in 1908. In 1920 the fineness was reduced to .800, and in 1967 to .500. During 1968 nickel completely replaced silver.

VICTORIA: The design by L.C. Wyon underwent a number of minor changes during the period. In 1880 both wide and narrow "0's" were used in the dates. The wide "0" is more valuable.

Narrow 0   Wide 0

VICTORIA 1870 - 1901

Date and Mint Mark	Mintage (1,000's)	Buying Price
1870	900	5.00
1871	400	6.00
1871H	748	6.00
1872H	2,240	4.00
1874H	1,600	4.00
1875H	1,000	100.00
1880H Narrow 0	400	6.00
1880H Wide 0	Incl.	25.00
1881H	820	4.00
1882H	600	5.00
1883H	960	4.00
1885	192	25.00
1886	540	4.00
1887	100	20.00
1888	400	4.00
1889	66	25.00
1890H	200	5.00
1891	120	10.00
1892	510	4.00

Date and Mint Mark	Mintage (1,000's)	Buying Price
1893	100	10.00
1894	220	4.00
1899	416	3.50
1900	1,320	3.50
1901	640	3.50

EDWARD VII: The coinage of Edward VII was designed by DeSaulles. In 1906 the reverse was modified by Blakemore to show re-engraved leaves and a larger crown.

EDWARD VII 1902 - 1910

Date and Mint Mark	Mintage (1,000's)	Buying Price
1902	464	2.50
1902H	800	2.50
1903	846	2.50
1904	400	3.50
1905	800	2.50
1906	1,238	2.50
1907	2,088	2.50
1908	495	2.50
1909	1,336	2.50
1910	3,578	2.50

GEORGE V: The obverse portrait and design by Sir Bertram MacKennal was combined with Blakemore's 1906 reverse. The issue of 1911 is "Godless." See the one-cent section for more information. The 1936 Dot issue was a small extra striking in 1937 from 1936 dies. Unlike the 1-cent and 10-cent pieces of the same issue, the 25-cent pieces were released for circulation.

GEORGE V 1911 - 1936

Date	Mintage (1,000's)	Buying Price
1911	1,721	5.00
1912	2,544	2.50
1913	2,214	2.50
1914	1,215	2.50
1915	242	3.50
1916	1.463	2.50
1917	3,366	2.50
1918	4,176	2.50
1919	5,852	2.50
1920	1,975	2.50
1921	597	3.50*
1927	468	6.00*
1928	2,114	2.50
1929	2,691	2.50
1930	969	2.50
1931	538	2.50
1932	538	2.50
1933	421	2.50
1934	384	2.50
1935	538	2.50
1936	972	2.50
1936 Dot	153	10.00

*All lettering and date must be clear.

GEORGE VI: The coinage of George VI was released in 1937. The obverse designed by T. Humphrey Paget was combined with a caribou head reverse pattern by Emmanuel Hahn. In early 1948, some of the coinage carried the 1947 with maple leaf date. See the one-cent section.

GEORGE VI 1937 - 1952

Date	Mintage (1,000's)	Buying Price
1937	2,690	2.50
1938	3,149	2.50
1939	3,532	2.50
1940	9,584	2.50
1941	6,654	2.50
1942	6,936	2.50
1943	13,560	2.50
1944	7,216	2.50
1945	5,296	2.50
1946	2,211	2.50
1947	1,525	2.50
1947 Maple Leaf	4,394	2.50
1948	2,564	2.50
1949	7,989	2.50
1950	9,673	2.50
1951	8,291	2.50
1952	8,860	2.50

ELIZABETH II: As with all other 1953 coinage, the initial dies were retouched by T. Shingles to create the "Shoulder Fold" variety. The new dies were used for coins of a slightly enlarged size, which were released at the same time as the normal issue. The larger coins have a slightly smaller date size and a wider rim.

The surface relief from 1954 to 1964 is very low, and circulated coins turn up worn to an undesirable degree.

In 1965 the "Mature Bust" of the Queen by Machin was introduced, and this was revised for the 1979 striking.

1965
Mature Bust

ELIZABETH II 1953 to date

Date		Mintage (1,000's)	Buying Price
1953	Large Date	10,457	2.50
1953	Small Date	Incl.	2.50
1954		2,319	2.50
1955		9,553	2.50
1956		11,269	2.50
1957		12,770	2.50
1958		9,337	2.50
1959		13,503	2.50
1960		22,835	2.50
1961		18,164	2.50
1962		29,559	2.50
1963		21,180	2.50
1964		36,479	2.50
1965		44,709	2.50
1966		25,626	2.50
1967	Wildcat	49,136	1.75
1968	.500 Fine Silver	71,464	1.00
1968	Nickel	88,869	.25
1969		133,038	.25
1970		10,302	.25
1971		48,170	.25
1972		43,743	.25

Large Bust
132 Obverse Beads

1973

Small Bust
120 Obverse Beads

Date		Mintage (1,000's)	Buying Price
1973	Small Bust	134,959	.25
1973	Large Bust	Incl.	60.00
1974		192,361	.25
1975		141,148	.25
1976		86,898	.25
1977		99,635	.25
1978		176,475	.25
1979		131,043	.25
1980		N/A	.25

FIFTY CENTS

The first Canadian 50-cent pieces were issued in 1870 in sterling silver weighing 11.62 grams. The weight was increased to 11.664 grams in 1908. The fineness was reduced to .800 in 1920. Coining in silver for 50-cent pieces ceased in 1967, although provision exists for coinage in .500 fine silver. In 1968 the 50-cent piece was minted in nickel and reduced slightly in size.

VICTORIA: The 50-cent piece of 1870, which was designed by L.C. Wyon, occurred in two varieties. The variety without the L.C.W. on the truncation is rare. It is further distinguished by the absence of a shamrock between the front cross of the diadem and the rose. On all issues with the initials on the bust this shamrock is present. All Victorian 50-cent pieces are rare.

VICTORIA 1870 - 1901

Date and Mint Mark	Mintage (1,000's)	Buying Price
1870 Without L.C.W.	450	100.00
1870 With L.C.W.	Incl.	25.00
1871	200	25.00
1871H	45	35.00
1872H	80	15.00

Date	Mintage (1,000's)	Buying Price
1881H	150	15.00
1888	60	45.00
1890H	20	175.00
1892	151	15.00
1894	29	75.00
1898	100	15.00
1899	50	30.00
1900	118	15.00
1901	80	15.00

EDWARD VII: The Edward VII 50-cent pieces were designed by G.W. DeSaulles. A modified reverse by W.H.J. Blakemore was used as well in 1910 creating two varieties for that year. The newer reverse showed somewhat different leaves in the wreath, with those immediately to the right of "CANADA" more sharply pointed than those on the earlier reverse.

EDWARD VII 1902 - 1910

Date and Mint Mark	Mintage (1,000's)	Buying Price
1902	120	5.00
1903H	140	7.00
1904	60	40.00
1905	40	35.00
1906	350	5.00
1907	300	5.00
1908	128	5.00
1909	203	5.00
1910	650	5.00

GEORGE V: The 50-cent piece of 1921 is very rare. The bulk of the 1921 issue was melted down eventually and recoined in 1929. Some very deceptive counterfeits of the 1921 coin exist. Most are altered dates, and a collector should always look for any sign of alteration. For instance, an alteration from 1931 will show a "2" that is abnormally large.

GEORGE V 1911 - 1936

Date	Mintage (1,000's)	Buying Price
1911	210	5.00
1912	286	5.00
1913	266	5.00
1914	160	6.00
1916	459	5.00
1917	752	5.00
1918	855	5.00
1919	1,113	5.00
1920	585	5.00
1921	206*	3,000.00
1929	228	5.00
1931	58	5,00
1932	19	25.00
1934	40	5.00
1936	39	5.00

*Majority were melted down, approximately 75 are known. Beware of altered date.

GEORGE VI: The George VI 50-cent piece was introduced in 1937. Paget's bust of the King and George Kruger-Gray's version of the Canadian coat-of-arms were used for the obverse and reverse, respectively.

GEORGE VI 1937 - 1952

Date	Mintage (1,000's)	Buying Price
1937	192	5.00
1938	192	5.00
1939	287	5.00
1940	1,997	5.00
1941	1,715	5.00
1942	1,974	5.00
1943	3,110	5.00
1944	2,460	5.00
1945	1,960	5.00
1946	950	5.00

The 1947 pieces were struck in two varieties. In the date either a long, straight "7" or a short, curved "7" was used. Both varieties also occurred in the maple leaf date issues. The long "7" was the same as the "7" used for 1937 coins. The short "7" is rarer, and altered numerals have been found.

1947 Straight "7"

Maple Leaf

No Maple Leaf

1947 Curved "7"

Maple Leaf

No Maple Leaf

Date	Mintage (1,000's)	Buying Price
1947 No Maple Leaf, Straight "7"	425	5.00
1947 No Maple Leaf, Curved "7"	Incl.	5.00
1947 Maple Leaf, Straight "7"	38	18.00
1947 Maple Leaf, Curved "7"	Incl.	450.00
1948	38	30.00
1949	859	5.00
1950	2,384	5.00
1951	2,422	5.00
1952	2,596	5.00

ELIZABETH II: During 1953 the original obverse design by Mary Gillick was re-engraved by Thomas Shingles. For more information see the one-cent section. The date on the George Kruger-Gray reverse was enlarged. Some coins were minted with the re-engraved obverse and the original reverse.

In 1955 the reverse was redrawn by Shingles and this smaller shield version was used until 1958. In 1959 a new reverse by Shingles was introduced. It displayed a different version of the coat-of-arms, one with a narrower, more pointed shield. In 1965 this reverse was combined with a new obverse by Machin. And in 1977 the obverse was modified by Patrick Brindley. In 1978 it was modified again.

No Shoulder Fold

Small Date

Shoulder Fold

Large Date

ELIZABETH II 1953 to date

Date	Mintage (1,000's)	Buying Price
1953	1,630	5.00
1954	506	5.00
1955	764	5.00
1956	1,379	5.00
1957	2,172	5.00
1958	2,957	5.00
1959	3,096	5.00
1960	3,489	5.00
1961	3,584	5.00
1962	5,208	5.00
1963	8,349	5.00
1964	9,178	5.00

New Obverse 1965   New Reverse 1959

Date	Mintage (1,000's)	Buying Price
1965	12,630	5.00
1966	7,683	5.00
1967 Wolf	4,211	5.00
1968	3,967	.50
1969	7,114	.50
1970	2,430	.50
1971	2,166	.50
1972	2,516	.50
1973	2,546	.50
1974	3,436	.50
1975	3,710	.50
1976	2,941	.50
1977	710	1.50
1978	3,342	.50
1979	3,425	.50
1980	N/A	.50

DOLLARS

Silver Dollars

Authority to coin dollars in silver was granted in 1910 and a pattern was struck the following year. However, it was not until 1935, the twenty-fifth anniversary of the reign of George V, that any coins of this denomination were struck. From 1935 until 1967 the dollar was minted in .800 fine silver with a weight of 23.327 grams. In 1968 it was coined in nickel at a reduced size. Since 1971 special commemorative dollars weighing 23.327 grams have been struck in .500 fine silver and sold in cases at a premium to collectors.

GEORGE V: The obverse of the Silver Jubilee dollar was designed by Percy Metcalfe. The voyageurs reverse design was by Emmanuel Hahn. In 1936 the obverse pattern was changed to the MacKennal bust of the King, which was used on all the other denominations of coins.

GEORGE V 1935 - 1936

Date	Mintage (1,000's)	Buying Price
1935	429	15.00
1936	340	15.00

53

GEORGE VI: The obverse for all issues was by T.H. Paget. The reverse for all the years except 1939 and 1949 was Hahn's voyageurs design. The 1939 reverse, also by Hahn, commemorated the Royal visit by showing the centre block of the Canadian Parliament Buildings. The 1949 dollar showed a portrayal of John Cabot's ship, "The Matthew," by T. Shingles, and commemorated the entrance of Newfoundland into the Dominion of Canada.

There was both a long and short "7" variety in 1947. The long "7" was the same "7" as was used in the 1937 dates, and it was the rarer variety. There was also a maple leaf date issue in 1947. Pending the arival of the 1948 dies with the altered Royal title, an issue was struck which had a leaf punched after the "7" of the short "7" 1947 reverse dies.

GEORGE VI 1937 - 1952

Date	Mintage (1,000's)	Buying Price
1937	207	15.00
1938	90	25.00
1939	1,364	10.00
1945	38	75.00
1946	93	20.00
1947 Short 7	66	40.00
1947 Long 7	Incl.	90.00
1947 Maple Leaf	21	100.00
1948	19	500.00
1949 "Matthew"	672	15.00

1947

Long 7

1947

Short 7

1947.

Maple Leaf

Royal Visit 1939   Ship Reverse 1949

Arnprior Dollars: Although the "Arnprior Dollars" were not true die varieties since they were the result of inadvertent over-polishing of the die surfaces, they were widely collected. Between 1950 and 1957 there were a number of variations in the water lines in front of and behind the canoe. The only issue which was a real die variety was the 1952 dollar with no water lines and an enlarged islet tip. The "Arnprior Dollars" were named after a shipment of dollars sent to Arnprior, Ontario. These dollars had only two and a half water lines. Beware of altered waterlines.

Arnprior

Regular

Date	Mintage (1,000's)	Buying Price
1950	261	10.00
1950 Arnprior	Incl.	10.00
1951	416	10.00

1952
Waterlines

1952
No Waterlines

Date	Mintage (1,000's)	Buying Price
1952 Waterlines	406	10.00
1952 No Waterlines	Incl.	10.00

ELIZABETH II: The 1953 to 1964 issues bore Gillick's laureate bust of the Queen. The obverse die was re-engraved by T. Shingles in 1953 to produce the well-known "Shoulder Fold" variety.

Hahn's voyageurs reverse was used every year except 1958 and 1964. The "Totem Pole" reverse dollar of 1958 which commemorated the formation of British Columbia as a Crown colony was designed by Stephan Trenka. The 1964 dollar which bore a heraldic floral design by Dinko Vodanovic commemorated the centenary of the Charlottetown and Quebec Conferences which led to Confederation in 1867.

ELIZABETH II 1953 to date

Date	Mintage (1,000's)	Buying Price
1953	1,073	10.00
1954	241	10.00
1955	260	10.00
1955 Arnprior	Incl.	50.00
1956	199	10.00
1957	481	10.00
1957 One Waterline	Incl.	10.00
1958 Totem Pole	3,040	10.00
1959	1,398	10.00
1960	1,338	10.00
1961	1,141	10.00
1962	1,636	10.00
1963	3,126	10.00
1964 Charlottetown	4,434	10.00
1965	7,864	10.00
1966	9,739	10.00
1967 Goose	5,816	10.00

British Columbia
Commemorative

Confederation Meetings
Commemorative

In 1965 the obverse was changed to the "Mature Bust" of the Queen. This design by Arnold Machin was redesigned by Patrick Brindley in 1973, and it was modified again in 1977. In 1965 the voyageurs reverse was completely redrawn, and in 1977 it was altered, for that year's issue only, by Terry Smith.

The reverse of the 1970 dollar by Raymond Taylor commemorated the centenary of Manitoba. The 1971 reverse commemorated the centenary of British Columbia's entrance into Confederation. It was drawn by Thomas Shingles. The dollar which commemorated Prince Edward Island's entrance into the Dominion of Canada was designed by Terry Manning and was issued in 1973. A dollar commemorating the first century of Winnipeg was designed by Paul Pederson and was minted in 1974. There were three varieties of the 1977 dollar. The rarest, Type 1, had a rounded edge and short waterlines in front of the canoe. The Queen's diadem was fully cut, and the jewel in the front was attached to the diadem. Type 2 had a square edge and longer waterlines, and the jewel was detached from the diadem. Type 3 also had a square edge, but the waterlines were short. The jewel was detached from the diadem.

Mature Bust
1965

Centennial of
Confederation

Nickel Dollars

Dollar coins for circulation were reduced in size and made of nickel from 1968.

Date	Mintage (1,000's)	Buying Price
1968	4,755	1.00
1969	4,215	1.00
1970 Manitoba	3,493	1.00
1971 British Columbia	3,659	1.00

Manitoba Centennial

B.C. Centennial

Date	Mintage (1,000's)	Buying Price
1972	2,193	1.00
1973 Prince Edward Island	2,683	1.00
1974 Winnipeg	2,268	1.00
1975	3,256	1.00
1976	1,717	1.00
1977	1,394	1.00
1978	2,948	1.00
1979	2,544	1.00
1980	N/A	1.00

P.E.I. Centennial

Winnipeg Centennial

GOLD COINS

There have been few gold issues in Canadian minting history.
The first gold coins struck in Canada were the 1908 Imperial
sovereigns. They were distinguished from the British issues by
the letter "C" just above the date. They were issued each year
until 1919, except for 1912 and 1915. There are imitations and
one should be careful when buying specimens from any year.

From 1912 to 1914 domestic $5 and $10 gold pieces were
minted. They are quite rare, especially the $5 gold from 1914,
and all these coins have been extensively counterfeited.

SOVEREIGNS

EDWARD VII 1908 - 1910

Date and Mint Mark	Mintage (1,000's)	Buying Price
1908C	636	1,000.00
1909C	16,273	200.00
1910C	28,012	200.00

GEORGE VI 1911 - 1919

Date and Mint Mark	Mintage (1,000's)	Buying Price
1911C	256,946	150.00
1913C	3,715	500.00
1914C	14,891	200.00
1916C	6,111	RARE
1917C	58,845	150.00
1918C	106,516	150.00
1919C	135,889	150.00

FIVE DOLLARS

GEORGE V 1912 - 1914

Date	Mintage (1,000's)	Buying Price
1912	165,680	175.00
1913	98,832	175.00
1914	31,122	400.00

TEN DOLLARS

GEORGE V 1912 - 1914

Date	Mintage (1,000's)	Buying Price
1912	74,759	400.00
1913	149,232	400.00
1914	140,068	425.00

Until the 1976 Olympic issues there had been no other gold coinage struck in Canada since 1914 except for the 1967 $20 piece. Two Olympic $100 gold pieces were struck for general sale, one in 14 karat and the other in 22 karat. Since 1976 all $100 issues have been proofs in 22 karat gold alloyed with silver and all are commemorative issues.

TWENTY DOLLARS

1967 Centennial
All coins were included in presentation sets. There was no separate issue.

Proof — $350.00

ONE HUNDRED DOLLARS

1976 Olympics

14k Unc. — $150.00

No beads around rim of coin.

22k Proof — $300.00

1977 Jubilee

22k Proof — $300.00

1978 Unity

22k Proof – $300.00

1979 Year of the Child

22k Proof – $300.00

1980 Arctic Territories

22k Proof - $300.00

FIFTY DOLLARS

22k Unc. – Price based on spot gold

1979 Maple Leaf

SPECIAL ISSUES

Proof-like and Specimen Silver Dollars

The Proof-like silver dollars made available by the mint from 1954 to 1967 are listed separately below, even though some were originally available only in sets. The mintage figures given below for these dates are for coins issued both separately and in sets.

After the changeover to nickel for the circulating coinage in 1968, Proof-like dollars were also only produced in nickel for three years.

Beginning in 1971 special issues of dollars in .500 fine silver were again made available to collectors as well as those in nickel. Most issues have been commemoratives, and all are of Specimen quality.

Date		Mintage (1,000's)	Buying Price
1954		5	100.00
1955		8	60.00
1955	Arnprior	Incl.	175.00
1956		10	50.00
1957		16	17.50
1958		33	17.50
1959		45	12.50
1960		82	12.50
1961		121	12.50
1962		249	12.50
1963		964	12.50
1964		2,862	12.50
1965		2,904	12.50
1966		673	12.50
1967		1,036	12.50
1968		1,408	1.00
1969		594	1.00
1970	Manitoba	646	1.25
1971	British Columbia, nickel	468	1.00
1971	British Columbia, silver	586	7.00
1972	Voyageur, nickel	406	1.00
1972	Voyageur, silver	342	6.00
1973	P.E.I., nickel	467	1.00
1973	R.C.M.P., silver	1,031	6.00
1974	Winnipeg, nickel	364	1.00
1974	Winnipeg, silver	729	6.00

Date	Mintage (1,000's)	Buying Price
1975 Voyageur, nickel	322	1.00
1975 Calgary, silver	931	6.00
1976 Voyageur, nickel	274	1.00
1976 Parliament Library, silver	579	8.00
1977 Senate Throne, silver	745	6.00
1978 XI Common. Games, silver	700	6.00
1979 Griffon, silver	827	6.00
1980 Arctic Territories, silver	N/A	6.00

Proof-like Sets

From 1954 to 1960 the mint issued sets of Proof-like coins in card holders. From 1961 to date the coins have been issued in pliofilm pouches. These Regular Sets contain six coins, one of each denomination.

Beginning in 1971, the mint also began offering Custom and Prestige Sets. Each Custom Set contains a full set of the coinage plus an extra cent to show the obverse. Prestige Sets contain a full, double-struck set of coinage plus an additional nickel dollar. Since 1973 the extra dollar in each set has been .500 fine silver.

Proof-like Regular Set Issued in Pliofilm Pouch 1961 to date

Regular Sets

Date		Mintage (1,000's)	Buying Price
1954		3	200.00
1955		6.3	120.00
1955	Arnprior	Incl.	250.00
1956		6.5	80.00
1957		11.9	32.00
1958		18	32.00
1959		31	20.00
1960		64	15.00
1961		98	15.00
1962		200	15.00
1963		673	15.00
1964		1,653	15.00
1965		2,904	15.00
1966		673	15.00
1967		964	15.00
1968		522	2.00
1969		326	2.00
1970	Manitoba	349	6.00
1971	British Columbia	253	2.50
1972	Voyageur	224	2.50
1973	R.C.M.P., Small Bust	244	4.00
1973	R.C.M.P., Large Bust	Incl.	200.00
1974	Winnipeg	312	3.75
1975	Voyageur	197	3.75
1976	Voyageur	172	6.00
1977	Senate Throne	225	6.00
1978	XI Common. Games	260	4.00
1979	Griffon	188	4.00
1980	Arctic Territories	N/A	4.00

Custom Double-Cent Sets

Date	Buy Price
1971	5.00
1972	5.00
1973	5.00
1974	5.00
1975	5.00
1976	5.00
1977	5.00
1978	5.00
1979	5.00
1980	5.00

Prestige Double-Dollar Sets

Date		Buy Price
1971		14.00
1972		30.00
1973	Small Bust	10.00
1973	Large Bust	200.00
1974		12.00
1975		11.00
1976		15.00
1977		20.00
1978		13.00
1979		13.00
1980		13.00

Specimen Sets

Sets of Specimen coins have been issued in Canada at various times since 1858, often in official cases. A representative selection follows.

1858 Victoria: 1¢, 5¢, 10¢, 20¢ 1,500.00
1870 Victoria: 5¢, 10¢, 25¢, 50¢ 3,000.00

The following sets are in leather or leatherette covered presentation cases.

1908 Edward VII: 1¢, 5¢, 10¢, 25¢, 50¢ 500.00
1911 George V: 1¢, 5¢, 10¢, 25¢, 50¢ 2,000.00
1937 George VI: 1¢, 5¢, 10¢, 25¢, 50¢, $1.00 ...... 400.00
1937 George VI: as above, but in card case 300.00
1967 Centennial Elizabeth II: 1¢, 5¢, 10¢, 25¢, 50¢
      $1.00, $20.00 gold 325.00
1967 Centennial Elizabeth II: as above, but
      with medal instead of $20.00 gold 30.00

1937 George VI Specimen Set

Olympic Coins and Sets

For the Olympic Games of 1976 seven series of silver coins were minted. There were four different coins in each series, two $5 and two $10 coins, struck in sterling silver. The $5 coins weighed 24.3 grams and the $10 coins weighed 48.6 grams. The coins were available, encapsulated in plastic, and in Custom, Prestige, and Proof sets.

SERIES I

1973	$5	Map of North America	Unc.	12.50
1973	$5	Kingston	Unc.	12.50
1973	$10	World Map	Unc.	25.00
1973	$10	Montreal	Unc.	25.00

Unc. Set .... 75.00   Proof Set 85.00

SERIES II

1974	$5	Athlete with Torch	Unc.	12.50
1974	$5	Olive Wreath	Unc.	12.50
1974	$10	Head of Zeus	Unc.	25.00
1974	$10	Temple of Zeus	Unc.	25.00

Unc. Set .... 75.00   Proof Set 85.00

SERIES III

1974	$5	Canoeing	Unc.	12.50
1974	$5	Rowing	Unc.	12.50
1974	$10	Lacrosse	Unc.	25.00
1974	$10	Bicycling	Unc.	25.00

Unc. Set .... 75.00   Proof Set 85.00

SERIES IV

1975	$5	The Marathon	Unc.	12.50
1975	$5	Ladies' Javelin	Unc.	12.50
1975	$10	Men's Hurdles	Unc.	25.00
1975	$10	Ladies' Shot Put	Unc.	25.00

Unc. Set .... 75.00   Proof Set 85.00

SERIES V

1975	$5	The Diver	Unc.	12.50
1975	$5	The Swimmer	Unc.	12.50
1975	$10	The Paddler	Unc.	25.00
1975	$10	Sailing	Unc.	25.00

Unc. Set .... 75.00   Proof Set 85.00

SERIES VI

1976	$5	Fencing	Unc.	12.50
1976	$5	Boxing	Unc.	12.50
1976	$10	Field Hockey	Unc.	25.00
1976	$10	Football	Unc.	25.00

Unc. Set .... 75.00   Proof Set 85.00

SERIES VII

1976	$5	Olympic Village	Unc.	12.50
1976	$5	Olympic Flame	Unc.	12.50
1976	$10	Olympic Stadium	Unc.	25.00
1976	$10	Olympic Velodrome	Unc.	25.00

Unc. Set .... 75.00   Proof Set 85.00

TOKENS

Canada has produced a great number of tokens of various kinds over the years. Tokens were used as a form of currency prior to the institution of the decimal currency system in 1858 (Colonial issues are not all tokens, some being regal coins). After Confederation, other kinds of tokens appeared, such as those for services, transportation and advertising purposes.

The prices in this section are for tokens in V.G. (Very Good) or F. (Fine) condition. Higher prices will be paid for rare issues or for tokens in V.F. (Very Fine) or better condition.

COLONIAL COINS AND TOKENS

French Regime

The French Regime coins are rare except for the copper issues of 1721-1722 and the 1738-1760 sol marques. These coins cannot be considered exclusively Canadian since they were distributed throughout the French colonies.

Sol 1738-1754 . . . . 2.00

Nova Scotia

In the early 19th century Nova Scotia was in short supply of currency, so to alleviate the problem a number of merchants imported tokens from England. These tokens in farthing, half-penny, and penny denominations were known as the "Trade and Navigation" tokens. Many of the private tokens were withdrawn from circulation after the issue of semi-regal coppers was begun in 1823. The tokens were called semi-regal because they were issued on local authority only. There were issues of pennies and halfpennies in 1824, 1832, 1840, and 1843. In 1856 Nova Scotia was authorized to produce regal coinage. Halfpenny and penny issues, called the Mayflower coinage, were released.

Nova Scotia Penny 1824-1856 .... .75

Nova Scotia Halfpenny 1823-1856 .... .50

White's Farthing 2.50

New Brunswick

There were very few different issues of New Brunswick tokens, perhaps because there was seldom a serious change shortage. There was a "For Public Accommodation" token issued in 1830. In 1843 the penny and halfpenny issues were without Imperial authority. The Imperial government objected to the idea of a local issue in New Brunswick; so until they authorized the New Brunswick issues of 1854 they were not told of the 1843 issue.

St. John Halfpenny 1830 .... 3.00

New Brunswick Penny 1843-1854 .... .75

New Brunswick Halfpenny 1843-1854 .... .50

Prince Edward Island

The first local issue of tokens in Prince Edward Island was the famous "Holey Dollar" and dumps. The local government authorized the perforation of 1,000 Spanish dollars and the countermarking of the resulting rings and plugs. The tokens were issued in 1813 and soon recalled because of numerous imitations.

The "Fisheries and Agriculture" halfpenny token was issued in 1858, and showed a steamboat on the obverse.

The "Sheaf of Wheat" halfpenny piece was struck in 1840 in very small quantities, and in the same year the first "Success to the Fisheries" halfpennies were introduced. Other tokens were issued in Prince Edward Island in 1855, 1857, and 1858, all of which are anonymous.

Ship 1.25

Plough .... .35

Self-Government
1855-1857 .... .50

Sheaf of Wheat
.... 30.00

Newfoundland

The "Rutherford Ram" token was introduced about 1840 in St. John's. The 1846 issue, which also used the ram design, was released from Harbour Grace. After 1850 large quantities of lightweight halfpenny tokens were brought in from Prince Edward Island and they quickly became the dominant copper coinage. The rare 1858 "Ship" halfpenny was issued by a St. John's merchant.

Rutherford Halfpenny .... .50

Ship 1858 .... 125.00

Lower Canada

The Magdalen Islands Penny token was issued for these islands in the St. Lawrence in 1815. It was never a popular issue and tokens in heavily worn condition puzzled numismatists until it was ascertained the tokens had been sent to Nova Scotia to help alleviate a copper shortage.

Magdalen Island Penny 1815 (if not badly worn) 3.50

Very few merchants in Lower Canada issued tokens in their own name. The earliest merchant token issued in the Montreal area was the now rare "Owens Ropery" which appeared in 1824. The Molson halfpenny token was designed, engraved, and struck in Montreal. The dies for this token are still in the possession of the Molson Company.

Owen's Ropery
.... 300.00

Molsons Halfpenny
.... 10.00

There were a number of bank issued tokens. The Bank of Montreal released the first bank tokens in Lower Canada, in 1835. These tokens, known as bouquet sou, were anonymous since the bank had no authority to issue in its own name until 1836. The tokens were immediately popular and a great many varieties of bouquet sou were issued.

In 1838 the Bank of Montreal was granted permission to import more copper. A new style of token showing a corner view of the bank was struck. The specimens of the "Side View" tokens struck in 1838-1839 were rejected by the bank because it was felt the workmanship and metal were not of good quality.

Bank of Montreal Side View Halfpenny 1838-1839 .... 45.00
Bank of Montreal Side View Penny 1838-1839 .... 100.00

Upper Canada

The first local tokens of Upper Canada were lightweight half-pennies issued in the memory of Sir Isaac Brock, killed at Queenston Heights in 1812.

Isaac Brock Halfpenny 1.00

It is likely that the Lesslie Twopence was issued in 1822. At that time a petition was being circulated to have the name of the town of York changed to Toronto, and Lesslie must have had his token inscribed in anticipation of the event. However, the petition was ignored by the lieutenant-governor and York was not renamed until 1834. It has been said the twopence token was not popular but well-worn specimens are known.

Lesslie Twopence 20.00

The Province of Upper Canada halfpenny piece (Britannia Halfpenny) was struck in 1832 by the same firm that struck the Nova Scotia coinage of 1832. Although it is felt the token was a government issue, it is not known if it was an official issue.

Province of Upper Canada Halfpenny 2.00

Province of Canada

In 1841 the Bank of Montreal was authorized to produce copper tokens for the recently formed Province of Canada. In 1842 it began to issue the "Front View" tokens, so named because they showed a front view of the bank. The penny issue dated 1837 may be a concoction rather than an official issue. The 1837 date tokens were lighter than the regular issue of 1842, and none were known before 1870.

In 1852 the Quebec Bank was permitted to issue copper tokens to relieve a serious copper shortage in Quebec City which had resulted from a delayed shipment from the Bank of Upper Canada (York). The traditional habitant obverse design was combined with a reverse showing the city seal.

Bank of Montreal Front View Halfpenny 1842-1844 .... .25
Bank of Montreal Front View Penny 1837 .... 35.00
Bank of Montreal Front View Penny 1842 .... .75
Quebec Bank Penny 1852 .... .35
Quebec Bank Halfpenny 1852 .... .25

The Bank of Upper Canada (York) issued copper from 1850 to 1857. The tokens of this bank were the most common official issues in colonial Canada. The tokens were not issued after the decimal currency system was adopted in 1858, but even so, when the bank failed in 1867 eleven tons of unissued penny and halfpenny tokens were found in the vaults.

Bank of Upper Canada Halfpenny 1850, 52, 54, or 57 20

Bank of Upper Canada Penny 1850, 52, 54 or 57 30

The Copper Company of Upper Canada halfpenny was a pattern struck at the instigation of Governor Simcoe. There was to be a new copper coinage but it was never produced. The so-called re-strikes were minted at a later date from different dies.

Copper Company of Canada Halfpenny (Proof) 75.00

British Columbia

The British Columbia gold coinage of 1862 is extremely rare. It was decided to coin gold from the Fraser River deposits, but such an issue might have breached the royal prerogative, so it was never struck. The existing specimens were struck as examples and never circulated. Collectors should be wary of recent brass copies that are gilded.

Pattern Gold $10 - Very Rare
Pattern Gold $20 - Very Rare

FUR TRADE TOKENS

North West Company

The North West Company was formed in 1784 to aid in the development and exploration of Canada's northern regions. The trade which the company carried on was based on beaver pelts. The company's token represented one pelt. All but one of the known specimens have a hole through them, and there are numerous counterfeit specimens.

North West Company Token 200.00

Hudson's Bay Company

The tokens for the Hudson's Bay Company were designed about 1854 and struck about 1857 in England. The tokens were introduced in northwest Canada during the period the Hudson's Bay Company administered it for the British government. The values struck on the tokens were to indicate parts of or whole adult beaver hides that were stretched and tanned. Beaver pelts were the basis of the commerce in that area of the country. The coins were never very popular, however, since the Indians found them to be easily lost.

Hudson's Bay Company Tokens
Set of Four (1, ½, ¼, ⅛) 60.00

TRANSPORTATION TOKENS

The first transportation tokens issued in Canada were used to pay tolls on the bridges joining Montreal Island to the mainland. The value varied depending upon the type of transport: foot, horse, carriage, or wagon.

Bridge Tokens 45.00/each

The Montreal & Lachine Railroad tokens were used by the workingmen and Indians who used the 3rd class compartment. The tokens were strung upon a wire when they were collected.

Montreal & Lachine Railroad Token 25.00

ADVERTISING PIECES

These examples were used in Nova Scotia and New Brunswick.

Purves 1.50

Blackley 1.50

McDermott 75.00

MISCELLANEOUS

The "Globe" tokens were issued first in 1879 for the purchase of the evening edition of the paper. At that time the tokens could be purchased at eight for ten cents. The Agincourt Dairy token represents issues of tokens which were released by a number of dairies and bakeries. The majority of these tokens have a small premium.

Evening Globe .... .50

Agincourt Dairy One Quart 7.50
Agincourt Dairy One Pint 7.50

During the American Civil War there was a shortage of change in Canada, so a number of merchants used postage stamps mounted in a brass frame and covered with a thin sheet of mica.

Weir and Larminie Encased Postage Stamps
1¢, 3¢, 5¢, or 10¢ 150.00

Anchor Money

A number of different tokens which were not intended for use in this colony had some circulation in Canada. The tokens like the "Anchor Money," or the "British Colonies" were intended for distribution in other British colonies. The "Anchor Money" was for use in Mauritius and the British West Indies, and the "British Colonies" for use in Jamaica.

1/2 Dollar	....	40.00
1/4 Dollar	....	1.25
1/8 Dollar	....	1.00
1/16 Dollar	....	1.00

CANADIAN MEDALS

The following selection of medals is comprised of Canadian war medals and commemorative medals. By "Canadian war medals" is meant medals awarded to Canadians only, or medals awarded in Canada. Canada followed the British system of honours as the need arose, embracing the three main categories of awards: Orders of Chivalry, Decorations, and Medals. The listings that follow are all of the latter category.

The responsibility for granting medals (and decorations) in Canada has changed over the years. In 1847 a board of officers at Montreal reviewed the applications from the Canadian militia made to the adjutant general of the militia for the award of the Military General Service Medal. In 1898 a new medals claim board was authorized to issue the Canada General Service Medal. Later, this board assumed the duty of reviewing applications and issuing long service medals when they were introduced in 1901. In 1919 another new medals board was formed which was responsible for reviewing and granting decorations, medals, and long service awards. Modifications to the board and new committees were gradually added over the years.

The commemorative medals shown in this guide represent the most common issues. As the names of these medals suggests, they were issued for significant historical events.

WAR MEDALS

Military General Service Medal
1793-1814

Fort Detroit Bar	$800.00
Chateauguay Bar	$800.00
Chrystler's Farm Bar	$800.00

**Canadian General Service Medal
1866-1870**

Fenian Raid Bar 1866 $125.00

Fenian Raid Bar 1870 $125.00

Red River Bar 1870 $150.00

**Egyptian Medal
1884-1885**

The Nile Bar $300.00

Kirbekan Bar $400.00

Khedive's Bronze Star

1884 . . . . $25.00

**North West Canada Medal
1885**

Medal Only $150.00

Saskatchewan Bar . $200.00

Queen's South Africa Medal
1899-1900

1899/1900 On Reverse $2,500.00
Dates Removed $75.00

King's South Africa Medal

1901-1902 .... $50.00

1914 Star
(only awarded to
2nd Field Hospital)

1914 Star $2,000.00

1914-15 Star

1914-15 Star $2.00

British War Medal

1919 .... $15.00

Allied Victory Medal

1919 .... $3.00

Merchantile Marine War Medal

1919 .... $15.00

Canadian Volunteer Service Medal

1943 . . . . $15.00

1939-1945 Star

1944 . . . . $3.00

Atlantic Star

1945 . . . . $3.00

Air Crew Europe Star

1945 . . . . $25.00

Africa Star

1943 .... $6.00

France & Germany Star

1945 .... $3.00

Italy Star

1945 .... $3.00

Pacific Star

1945 .... $3.00

Burma Star

1945 .... $3.00

Defence Medal

1945 .... $15.00

1939-1945 War Medal

1946 .... $15.00

Canadian Korean War Medal

1951 .... $25.00

**United Nations
Emergency Force Medal**

1956 .... $15.00

**United Nations Medal
(Various)**

1960 to present $15.00

International Commission Medal

1967 .... $30.00

United Nations Korea Medal

1950 (French & English) $20.00

International Commission Medal

1973 .... $30.00

COMMEMORATIVE MEDALS

King George V Coronation Medal

1911 .... $25.00

King George V Silver Jubilee Medal

1935 .... $15.00

King George VI Coronation Medal

1937 .... $15.00

**Queen Elizabeth II
Coronation Medal**

1953 . . . . $15.00

**Queen Elizabeth II
Silver Jubilee Medal**

1978 . . . . $15.00

Canadian Centennial Medal

1967 . . . . $30.00

PAPER MONEY OF CANADA

Introduction

Collectors of Canadian paper money have much from which to choose. The earliest banks, both chartered and private, issued their own notes, as did many merchants. The most popular notes with collectors have been those which were issued by the various provincial governments and by the federal government after Confederation. Most of the paper money now in circulation is issued by our central bank, the Bank of Canada.

In the examples of Canadian paper money which follow, the main or central vignettes, front and back, are described, along with the denomination and date. Prices are given for the most commonly encountered variety of the note.

Collectors of paper money should also be familiar with the following characteristics:

Signature Details: Signatures appear on notes in handwritten manuscript form (mss); and/or printed engraved (engr) or typographed engraved (typed) form.

Imprint: This indicates the company that engraved the plates and/or printed the notes from them.

Overprints and Stamps: Overprints are extra details added by a printing press to the note after the printing is otherwise complete. Stamps differ from overprints in that they are added by hand.

Protectors: These are coloured overprints which give the denomination of the note and serve as an anti-counterfeiting device. They can occur in word form ("one") or numeral form ("1").

For the most part, the selections of paper money which follow are of completed notes, that is, those which were fully signed, numbered and dated and then put into circulation. In some rare cases, the following forms of a particular note are more commonly known:

Remainder: A regular note which has not had all the blanks filled in, whether they be dates, signatures, or otherwise.

Specimen: A printing not intended for circulation, but to acquaint bank employees and others with the characteristics of genuine notes. Frequently, specimens are printed with a serial number comprised of a series of "0's" and overprinted "SPECIMEN."

Proof: A trial or sample impression taken from the printing plates on very thin card-backed paper. They often have no serial number and may or may not be overprinted "SPECIMEN."

In addition to genuine notes, the collector may also come across fraudulent examples:

Counterfeit: A facsimile copy of a legitimate bank note.
Spurious: A note that is of a design that does not correspond to any notes issued by a legitimate bank. Spurious notes can purport to be redeemable at a legitimate or a phantom bank.
Altered: In a Canadian context, a genuine note on which the name of the bank has been fraudulently changed to that of another bank.
Raised: A note which has been fraudulently modified so as to appear to be of a higher denomination.

GRADING

Grading is an important part of collecting, though often a matter of opinion. The following grading guide is an accurate indication of the requirements used by many dealers. Grading should be done under good and constant illumination. Each side of the note should be examined separately under direct lighting. Sometimes flaws which are not evident on the face of a note are visible on the back. As well, each side of the note should be examined with a light at an angle to the surface of the note. To do this, place the note on the palm of your hand and point your fingers at the light. You will be able to look lengthwise up the surface of the note towards the light. This will make the light rays glance off any surface flaws, slight creases or folds, and any areas of wear on the paper will become immediately noticeable.

Unc. - Uncirculated. A perfect note. Crisp and clean as when new and without any creases or pinholes. Colours have original brightness.
E.F. - Extremely Fine. Crisp and clean as when new, but with minor creases or pinholes. Colours have original brightness.
V.F. - Very Fine. Fairly crisp and clean, but with some creases and other signs of having been in circulation. No serious soiling or fading of colours.

F. - Fine. A well circulated note but still firm with little soiling or fading of colours.

V.G. - Very Good. A whole note, with some signs of edge fraying, damaged corners and perhaps some soiling and fading of colours. Some wear is evident at creases.

G. - Good. Very worn and creased, fraying edges and soiled and slightly torn where folded. Note is soft or limp.

- Fair. Badly worn, ragged edges, torn, dirty, faded and generally unattractive.

In addition, to accurately grade a note it is necessary to describe any other defects, which might include:

1. Minor counting creases or edge defects.
2. Tears or signature perforations.
3. Serious stains, smudges or crayon marks.
4. Missing corners, cut and punch cancellations or edge defects.
5. Undesirable rubber stamps.
6. Any repairs, such as sticky tape.
7. Chemical damage, paste or glue from attachment to a page.
8. Poorly centred or badly trimmed edges.
9. Unsigned or undated remainder notes.
10. Proofs and specimen notes are commonly accepted as being in uncirculated condition. Otherwise, they should be described as impaired with the type and degree of impairment stated.

HANDLING AND CLEANING

Inexperienced collectors should always use great care when handling notes. Notes should be handled as little as possible, since oil and perspiration from one's skin can damage and devalue a note. Care should be taken to ensure that unfolded or uncreased notes remain so, and that even marginal tears or abrasions are avoided. Under no circumstances should one ever wash or otherwise try to clean a note since it is quite likely that the note's value will be considerably reduced. The same is true for ironing or pressing. It should be avoided.

Province of Canada

In 1859 legislation for a government note issue was introduced, criticized, and abandoned. It was revised in 1866, then revised and passed as the Provincial Notes Act of 1866. By this Act, the government was authorized to issue notes not to exceed $8 million in total, which were redeemable on demand, in specie (gold), in Toronto and Montreal. The notes were issued through The Bank of Montreal.

$1 1866

Face: Coat-of-Arms of the Province of Canada with sailor and farmer

Back: Lathework, counters and Provincial name

$2 1866

Face: Seated Britannia with two allegorical women and boys

Back: Lathework, counters and Provincial name

$5 1866

Face: Coat-of-Arms of the Province of Canada with Indian princess and lion

Back: Lathework, counters and Provincial name

$10 1866

Face: Crowned lion, sheaf of wheat, train, anchor and sailing ships

Back: Lathework, counters and Provincial name

$20 1866

Face: Two beavers building
a dam
Back: Lathework, counters
and Provincial name

$50 1866

Face: Mercury holding map
of British North
America, harbour,
ships, train
Back: Lathework, counters
and Provincial name

Denom.	Issue Date	Buy Price V.G.
$ 1	Oct. 1, 1866	150.00
$ 2	Oct. 1, 1866	225.00
$ 5	Oct. 1, 1866	350.00
$10	Oct. 1, 1866	600.00
$20	Oct. 1, 1866	600.00
$50	Oct. 1, 1866	650.00

Dominion of Canada

FRACTIONAL CURRENCY

Fractional currency was first issued in 1870 as a temporary substitute for silver coin. The government had begun to withdraw American silver from circulation and replace it with a domestic silver coinage. In the meantime 25-cent notes were issued. The notes proved popular as a means of sending small sums of money through the mail, and demand for them caused the government to issue a second series beginning in 1900. In 1923 a third series was issued, and these "shinplasters" were particularly useful between 1922 and 1926 when no Canadian silver was issued. These notes were issued until 1935. No fractional currency has been issued since 1935, the year the Bank of Canada began to issue its notes.

25¢ 1870

Face: Britannia
Back: Lathework and
redeemability
information

25¢ 1900

Face: Britannia seated on
her shield, sailing
ship in background
Back: Lathework and
counters

25¢ 1923

Face: Britannia holding her
trident
Back: Lathework and
counters

Denom.	Issue Date	Variety	Buy Price V.G.
25¢	1870	Plain	2.50
25¢	1870	A Series	14.00
25¢	1870	B Series	2.75
25¢	1900	Courtney signature, left	2.00
25¢	1900	Boville signature, left	2.00
25¢	1900	Saunders signature, left	2.00
25¢	1923	Hyndman/Saunders signatures	3.00
25¢	1923	McCavour/Saunders signatures	2.00
25¢	1923	Campbell/Clark signatures	2.00

DOMINION OF CANADA NOTES

Before the Bank of Canada was established, the responsibility for paper currency was shared by the government and the chartered banks. The government issued fractional currency and all $1 and $2 notes. From 1882 to 1902 $4 notes were issued, and after 1912 $5 notes. These government notes, issued by the Department of Finance, are known as Dominion of Canada notes. Dominion of Canada $50 and $100 notes were issued in 1872, and $500 and $1000 notes appeared in 1871, 1911, and 1925. These notes are all very rare. The chartered banks issued $4, $5, $10, $20, $50, and $100 notes. There are also some odd denominations, such as $6 and $7 notes. After 1871 the banks were not permitted to issue notes in denominations that were not even multiples of $5.

Since Canadian currency was not standardized before 1881, the notes can bear several different inscriptions, such as "Payable in Toronto," or Montreal, or Halifax, or Saint John, or Victoria, or the Province of Manitoba. Notes payable in Victoria are legendary today; only one $1 note is known to have survived, and no $2 notes.

One Dollar Notes

$1 1870

Face: Allegorical female pointing to Canada's location on a globe

Back: Lathework, counters and city name

$1 1878

Face: Countess of Dufferin
Back: Great Seal of Canada

$1 1897, 1898

Face: Logging on a Canadian river
Back: Parliament Building

$1 1911

Face: Earl of Grey,
Countess of Grey
Back: Parliament Building

$1 1917

Face: Princess Patricia
Back: Parliament Building

$1 1923

Face: King George VI
Back: Library of
Parliament

Denom.	Issue Date	Variety	Buy Price V.G.
$1	1870	Montreal	75.00
$1	1878	Lettered, Montreal	22.00
$1	1897		40.00
$1	1898	Courtney, r; ONE's curved outward	8.00
$1	1911	Green line	7.00
$1	1917	Various-Boville, ONE	6.00
$1	1923	McCavour-Saunders, black seal	5.00

Two Dollar Notes

$2 1870

Face: Indian chief on bluff
watching train below
Back: Lathework, counters
and city name

$2 1878

Face: Earl of Dufferin
Back: Great Seal of Canada
and city name

$2 1887

Face: Marchioness &
Marquis of
Lansdowne
Back: Cartier's arrival at
Quebec

$2 1897

Face: Six men in fishing
dory
Back: Agricultural industry
allegory

$2 1914

Face: Duke & Duchess of
Connaught
Back: Coat-of-Arms of
Canada

$2 1923

Face: Edward, Prince of
Wales in uniform of
the Welsh guards
Back: Coat-of-Arms of
Canada

Denom.	Issue Date	Variety	Buy Price V.G.
$2	1870	Montreal	225.00
$2	1878	Montreal	200.00
$2	1887		75.00
$2	1897	Courtney, r; dark brown back	20.00
$2	1914	Various-Boville, curved wording	9.00
$2	1923	Campbell-Clark; black seal	7.00

Four Dollar Notes

$4 1882

Face: Marquis of Lorne
Back: Lathework, counters and Dominion name

$4 1900, 1902

Face: Sault Ste. Marie locks
Back: Parliament Buildings and Library

Denom.	Issue Date	Variety	Buy Price V.G.
$4	1882		150.00
$4	1900		65.00
$4	1902	Courtney, r; large FOUR's	65.00

Five Dollar Notes

$5 1912

Face: Passenger train travelling through the Wentworth Valley
Back: Lathework, counters and Dominion name

$5 1924

Face: Queen Mary in official court dress of consort
Back: East Block, Parliament Buildings

Denom.	Issue Date	Variety	Buy Price V.G.
$5	1912	Various-Boville	30.00
$5	1924		135.00

Fifty Dollar Notes

$50 1870

Face: Mercury holding a map of British North America
Back: Lathework, counters and city name

Denom.	Issue Date	Variety	Buy Price V.G.
$50	1870	Montreal	RARE

Bank of Canada

1935 ISSUES

In 1935 the Bank of Canada began to issue paper money. Under the legislation creating the bank, it became the sole bank of issue in Canada. The chartered banks were given until 1950 to withdraw their notes from circulation. In 1950 they paid the government an amount equal to the value of their notes still outstanding. The government then became responsible for the redemption of any chartered bank notes still in circulation.

The Bank of Canada notes were smaller than the Dominion of Canada notes. In 1935 a $25 note to commemorate the Silver Jubilee of the reign of King George V and the first bills with French inscriptions were issued.

$1 1935

Face: King George V
Back: Agriculture allegory

$2 1935

Face: Queen Mary
Back: Transportation allegory

$5 1935

Face: Prince of Wales
Back: Electric Power allegory

$10 1935

Face: Princess Mary
Back: Harvest allegory

$20 1935

Face: Princess Elizabeth
Back: Toiler allegory

$25 1935

Face: King George V and
       Queen Mary
Back: Windsor Castle

$50 1935

Face: Prince Albert, Duke of
       York
Back: Modern Inventions
       allegory

$100 1935

Face: Prince Henry, Duke of
       Gloucester
Back: Commerce and
       Industry allegory

Denom.	Issue Date	Variety	Buy Price V.G.
$ 1	1935	English text	2.00
$ 1	1935	French text	3.00
$ 2	1935	English text	7.00
$ 2	1935	French text	15.00
$ 5	1935	English text	10.00
$ 5	1935	French text	12.00
$ 10	1935	English text	12.00
$ 10	1935	French text	15.00
$ 20	1935	English text, small seal	25.00
$ 20	1935	French text	25.00
$ 25	1935	English text	200.00
$ 25	1935	French text	350.00
$ 50	1935	English text	75.00
$ 50	1935	French text	100.00
$100	1935	English text	125.00
$100	1935	French text	175.00

1937 ISSUES

The first bilingual bank notes were issued in 1937. The printing of bilingual notes made it unnecessary to engrave duplicate sets of plates. The $25 and $500 notes were discontinued.

The English inscription is on the left, the French is on the right. The serial number appears twice on the face of each note to the right and left of the central vignette. The serial number is comprised of two prefix letters and seven digits. The upper letter is for the series; the lower letter is for the denomination.

The prefix letters are used in the following manner:

Upper-Series

A, B, C, D, E, H, J, K, L, M, N, O, R, S, T, U, W, X, Y, Z

Lower-Denomination

A - $1   E - $20
B - $2   H - $50
C - $5   J - $100
D - $10   K - $1000

F & G were added only to the M series with the Gordon-Towers signatures.

$1 1937

Face: King George VI
Back: Agriculture allegory

$2 1937

Face: King George VI
Back: Harvest allegory

$5 1937

Face: King George VI
Back: Electric Power allegory

$10 1937

Face: King George VI
Back: Transportation
allegory

$20 1937

Face: King George VI
Back: Fertility allegory

— **$50 1937**

Face: King George VI
Back: Modern Inventions
allegory

$100 1937

Face: Sir John A. Macdonald
Back: Commerce and
Industry allegory

Denom.	Issue Date	Variety	Buy Price Unc.
$ 1	1937	Gordon-Towers	5.00
$ 2	1937	Gordon-Towers	15.00
$ 5	1937	Gordon-Towers	15.00
$ 10	1937	Gordon-Towers	17.50
$ 20	1937	Gordon-Towers	25.00
$ 50	1937	Gordon-Towers	65.00
$100	1937	Gordon-Towers	125.00

1954 ISSUES

The issue of 1954 was also bilingual. The notes of this series are slightly longer and narrower than the preceeding issues.

The serial numbers are printed twice in red on the top colour areas, on the face of the note, once on each side. Two letters preceed the serial number on each note for the purpose of identifying both the denomination and series. The lower letter designates the denomination, and the upper, the series. The denomination letters are:

$ 1 - A, L, M $ 20 - E
$ 2 - B, R $ 50 - H
$ 5 - C $ 100 - J
$ 10 - D, T $1000 - K

For the series letters, all of the letters of the alphabet, except Q, were used, each letter being used for ten million notes. The note number will not exceed seven digits except in the case of the ten millionth note which will have eight digits.

Starting with this issue of Bank of Canada notes, if a serial number or any other detail of the note was spoiled, a replacement note was issued. The replacement notes have a small asterisk placed just before the serial number. Asterisk serial numbers only exist on the $1 to $20 notes in this issue.

"DEVIL'S FACE" PORTRAIT

All notes of this issue have the Queen's portrait on the face. By chance, the first portrait used had the hair shaded such that it appeared that the light areas were the features of a "devil" peering out from behind the Queen's ear and notes with this portrait came to be called "devil's face" notes.

The portrait of the Queen with a "devil's face" outlined in her hair generated almost instant controversy. The portrait was modified by darkening the light in the hair and thus removing the shading which had resulted in the "devil."

$1 1954

Face: Queen Elizabeth II
Back: Western Prairie and sky

$2 1954

Face: Queen Elizabeth II
Back: Country valley in central Canada

$5 1954

Face: Queen Elizabeth II
Back: Northern stream and forest

$10 1954

Face: Queen Elizabeth II
Back: Rocky Mountain peak

$20 1954

Face: Queen Elizabeth II
Back: Laurentians in winter

$50 1954

Face: Queen Elizabeth II
Back: Atlantic seashore

Denom.	Issue Date	Variety	Buy Price Unc.
$ 1	1954	Modified, Beattie-Rasminsky	1.10
$ 2	1954	Modified, Beattie-Rasminsky	2.20
$ 5	1954	Devil's Face, Beattie-Coyne	20.00
$ 10	1954	Modified, Beattie-Rasminsky	15.00
$ 20	1954	Devil's Face, Beattie-Coyne	30.00
$ 50	1954	Modified, Beattie-Rasminsky	60.00
$100	1954	Modified, Beattie-Rasminsky	110.00

$1 CENTENNIAL 1967

For the centennial of Canada's Confederation a special $1 note was issued. The note had a single design and two types of serial numbers, regular serial numbers and a special number 1867-1967. The special series was available from the Bank of Canada as a collector's item, but examples were soon found in circulation. In addition there was an asterisk series for replacement notes.

Replacement

Regular

Commemorative

111

Denom.	Issue Date	Variety	Buy Price Unc.
$1	1967	Commemorative serial number	1.10
$1	1967	Regular serial number	1.25
$1	1967	Asterisk serial number	3.00

1969 - 1975 MULTICOLOUR ISSUE

This new series combined fine line engraving with subtle colour variations to make notes that are extremely difficult to counterfeit. The series features a new portrait of the Queen, and portraits of some of the previous prime ministers of Canada. To date the notes from $1 through $100 have been released in both regular and asterisk issues. There are no plans for a new $1000 note issue. The first notes issued in the series were the $20 dated 1969 (despite their date they were released first in June, 1970).

The serial number appears twice on the face of the notes, upper left in red and upper right in blue.

$1 1973

Face: Queen Elizabeth II
Back: Parliament Buildings
from Ottawa River

$2 1974

Face: Queen Elizabeth II
Back: Inuit on ice floes

$5 1972

Face: Sir Wilfred Laurier
Back: West Coast salmon
fishing

$10 1971
Face: Sir John A. Macdonald
Back: Oil refinery

$20 1969
Face: Queen Elizabeth II
Back: Rocky Mountain lake

$50 1975
Face: William Lyon
       Mackenzie King
Back: R.C.M.P. Musical Ride

$100 1975
Face: Sir Robert Borden
Back: East Coast fishing fleet

Denom.	Issue Date	Variety	Buy Price Unc.
$ 1	1973	Lawson-Bouey	1.00
$ 2	1974	Lawson-Bouey	2.00
$ 5	1972	Lawson-Bouey	5.00
$ 10	1971	Lawson-Bouey	10.00
$ 20	1969	Lawson-Bouey	20.00
$ 50	1975	Lawson-Bouey	50.00
$100	1975	Lawson-Bouey	100.00

1979 ISSUES

The series beginning in 1979 is a modification of the previous issue. The face designs are similar, as is the colouration. The serial numbers are moved to the back of the note at the bottom where the name of the Bank of Canada previously appeared. The black serial numbers are machine readable. To date only the $5 and $20 notes have been released.

$5 1979
Face: Sir Wilfred Laurier
Back: Salmon fishing on the West Coast

$20 1979
Face: Queen Elizabeth II
Back: Lake and Rocky Mountains

Denom.	Issue Date	Buy Price Unc.
$ 5	1979	5.00
$20	1979	20.00

Alberta Prosperity Certificate

The notes usually have one or more 1¢ stamps on the back. The original intention was to redeem each note after 104 stamps had been put on the back. Each person or firm handling a note was required to affix a stamp. Of the 357,680 issues, all but 19,639 were redeemed.

$1 1936

$1 1936 (back)

Denom.	Issue Date	Buy Price V.G.
$1	1936	10.00

Newfoundland Government
Cash Notes
1901 - 1914

I. DEPARTMENT OF PUBLIC WORKS TYPE

40¢ 1901-1909

Denom.	Issue Date	Buy Price V.G.
40¢	1901-09	35.00
50¢	1901-09	35.00
80¢	1901-09	50.00
$1	1901-09	75.00
$5	1901-09	125.00

II. DOUBLE DATE OR MULTICOLOURED TYPE

$1 1910-1914

Denom.	Issue Date	Buy Price V.G.
25¢	1910-14	10.00
50¢	1910-14	10.00
$1	1910-14	20.00
$2	1910-14	50.00
$5	1910-14	100.00

Newfoundland Government
Government Notes
1920

$1 1920

$2 1920

Denom.	Issue Date	Buy Price V.G.
$1	1920	15.00
$2	1920	20.00

Canadian Bank Notes

The vast majority of chartered bank notes have premium value, and while it is not possible to list all issues due to the space limitations, a representative selection is provided. Negotiable notes are indicated by an asterisk. Others are not negotiable, but as collectors items often have premium value.

THE BANK OF ACADIA 1872 - 1873

$4 1872
Face: Cherubs and ornate 4
Back: Lathework and
counters
V.G. $40.00

THE AGRICULTURAL BANK, Toronto 1834 - 1837

$1 (5s) 1834-1835
Face: Horse
Back: Plain
V.G. $5.00

$2 (10s) 1834-1835
Face: Beehive, cornucopia,
sheaf, spinning wheel
Back: Plain
V.G. $5.00

*BARCLAY'S BANK (CANADA)   1929 - 1956

$5 1929
Face: Seated female with
globe
Back: Bank building

$10 1929

Face: Seated female with globe
Back: Bank building

$20 1929

Face: Seated female with globe
Back: Bank building

Denom.	Issue Date	Variety	Buy Price V.G.
$ 5	1929	Large size note	75.00
$10	1929	Large size note	60.00
$20	1929	Large size note	100.00
$ 5	1935	Small size note, design as 1929	15.00
$10	1935	Small size note, design as 1929	17.50

THE BANK OF BRANTFORD 1857 - 1860's

$4 1859

Face: Unloading wagon at canal, mill in background
Back: Plain

V.G. $10.00

(Issued in both red & green tints)

*THE BANK OF BRITISH COLUMBIA 1862 - 1901

$5 1894

Face: Britannia and seated woman, mountains in background
Back: Lathework, counters and bank name
.
V.G. $500.00

118

*THE BANK OF BRITISH NORTH AMERICA
1836-1918

$5 1884

Face: Queen Victoria
Back: Lathework, counters
and bank name

$5 1886

Face: Bank Crest
Back: Bank Crest

$10 1889

Face: Queen Victoria
Back: Bank Crest

$5 1911

Face: King George V
Back: Bank Crest

$10 1911

Face: Queen Mary
Back: Bank Crest

$20 1911

Face: King Edward VII
Back: Bank Crest

119

Denom.	Issue Date	Variety	Buy Price V.G.
$ 5	1884		250.00
$ 5	1886	Mss. signature, r.	20.00
$10	1889	Mss. signature, r.	30.00
$ 5	1911	Mackenzie signature, r.	50.00
$10	1911	Mackenzie signature, r.	50.00
$20	1911	Mackenzie signature, r.	200.00

CANADA BANK 1792

5s 1792

Face: Beaver gnawing at
stump

Back: Plain

V.G. $250.00

THE BANK OF CANADA 1818 - 1831

There is no relation between this bank and the present Bank of Canada.

$1 1818-1819

Face: Seated woman with
cornucopia and left
hand on 1

Back: Plain

V.G. $50.00

$2 1822

Face: Seated woman with
cornucopia and left
hand on 2

Back: Plain

V.G. $50.00

*THE CANADIAN BANK OF COMMERCE
1867 - 1961

$1 1867

Face: Woman on shell
      pulled by dolphins
Back: Lathework, counters
      and bank name

$5 1888-1912

Face: Woman with books,
      lamp
Back: Lathework, counters
      and bank name

$10 1888-1912

Face: Helmeted woman's
      head with cherubs
Back: Lathework, counters
      and bank name

$20 1888-1912

Face: Bank Seal
Back: Lathework, counters
      and bank name

$5 1917

Face: Allegorical group:
      "Agriculture",
      Mercury,
      "Invention"
Back: Bank Seal

$10 1917

Face: Pastoral landscape:
      Juno with bull,
      Ceres, goat herd
Back: Bank Seal

$20 1917

Face: Seascape: Neptune, seamaidens, Mercury and maiden
Back: Bank Seal

$50 1917

Face: Industry: Vulcan, Herculean youths
Back: Bank Seal

Denom.	Issue Date	Variety	Buy Price V.G.
$ 1	1867		150.00
$ 5	1912	Mss. signature, r.	20.00
$10	1907		20.00
$20	1912	Mss. signature, r.	50.00
$ 5	1917	Multicoloured seal	10.00
$ 5	1917	Green tint	20.00
$10	1917	White background	12.00
$10	1917	Orange tint	12.00
$20	1917	White background	22.00
$20	1917	Yellow tint	22.00
$50	1917	White background	75.00
$50	1917	Olive tint	60.00
$ 5	1935	Small size note, design as 1917	6.00
$10	1935	Small size note, design as 1917	11.00
$20	1935	Small size note, design as 1917	22.00

BANQUE CANADIENNE 1836 - 1838

$1 1836

Face: Cornucopia, sheaf and spinning wheel
Back: Habitant
V.G. **$50.00**

BANQUE CANADIENNE NATIONALE 1924 - 1979

$5 1929

Face: Monument
Back: Provincial Crests

$10 1929

Face: Monument
Back: Provincial Crests

$20 1929

Face: Monument
Back: Provincial Crests

$50 1929

Face: Maisonneuve
    monument
Back: Provincial Crests

Denom.	Issue Date	Variety	Buy Price V.G.
$ 5	1929	Large size note	10.00
$10	1929	Large size note	12.50
$20	1929	Large size note	30.00
$50	1929	Large size note	100.00
$ 5	1935	Small size note, design as 1929	7.00
$10	1935	Small size note, design as 1929	11.00

THE CITY BANK, Montreal 1833 - 1876

$1 1857

Face: Queen Victoria
(Chalon portrait)
on Crest

Back: Scrollwork with
"CITY BANK/
MONTREAL"

$2 1857

Face: Paddle wheel steamship and boats, city in
background

Back: Scrollwork with
"CITY BANK/
MONTREAL"

$4 1857

Face: Crest with woman
and farmer

Back: Scrollwork with
"CITY BANK/
MONTREAL"

Denom.	Issue Date	Variety	Buy Price V.G.
$1	1857	Orange back	100.00
$2	1857	Orange back	125.00
$4	1857	Orange back	200.00

THE BANK OF CLIFTON 1859 - 1863

$1 1859

Face: Roebling Bridge
Back: Plain

$1 1860-1861
Face: St. George slaying
dragon
Back: Plain

$2 1860-1861
Face: St. George slaying
dragon
Back: Plain

$5 1860-1861
Face: St. George slaying
dragon
Back: Plain

Denom.	Issue Date	Variety	Buy Price V.G.
$1	1859	Fully engraved date	5.00
$1	1860-1861		5.00
$2	1860-1861		5.00
$5	1860-1861		5.00

THE COLONIAL BANK OF CANADA 1856 - 1863

$3 1859
Face: Three allegorical
women
Back: Plain
V.G. $15.00

$4 1859
Face: Queen Victoria
(Winterhalter
portrait)
Back: Plain
V.G. $10.00

*COMMERCIAL BANK OF NEWFOUNDLAND
1857 - 1894

$2 1888

Face: Seated "Commerce"
figure
Back: Lathework, counters
and bank name

V.G. $40.00

$5 1888

Face: Seated "Commerce"
figure
Back: Lathework, counters
and bank name

V.G. $50.00

THE CONSOLIDATED BANK OF CANADA
1876 - 1879

$4 1876

Face: Bank Seal in
modified Royal Crest
Back: Lathework, counters
and bank name

$5 1876

Face: Bank Seal in
modified Royal Crest
Back: Lathework, counters
and bank name

$10 1876

Face: Bank Seal in
modified Royal Crest
Back: Lathework, counters
and bank name

Denom.	Issue Date	Buy Price V.G.
$ 4	1876	75.00
$ 5	1876	75.00
$10	1876	50.00

*THE CROWN BANK OF CANADA   1904 - 1908

$5 1904

Face: Cattle in pasture
Back: Crown and floral
symbols

V.G. $600.00

*THE DOMINION BANK   1869 - 1955

$4 1871

Face: Farmer pumping
water for livestock
Back: Lathework, counters
and bank name

$5 1896-1925

Face: Kneeling woman with
anvil
Back: Greek god

$10 1900-1925

Face: Seated Britannia,
lion
Back: Beaver

$20 1897-1923

Face: Seated woman with
sheaf and tools
Back: Bust of Greek
goddess

127

$5 1931

Face: Austin - Bogert
Back: Map of Canada

$10 1931

Face: Austin - Bogert
Back: Map of Canada

$5 1935

Face: Danson - Carlisle
Back: Map of Canada

$10 1935

Face: Danson - Carlisle
Back: Map of Canada

$5 1938

Face: Carlisle - Rae
Back: Map of Canada

$10 1938

Face: Carlisle - Rae
Back: Map of Canada

Denom.	Issue Date	Variety	Buy Price V.G.
$ 4	1871		400.00
$ 5	1925		20.00
$10	1925	Nanton signature, r.	20.00
$20	1925		30.00
$ 5	1931	Bogert signature, r.	7.00
$10	1931	Bogert signature, r.	12.00
$ 5	1935		7.00
$10	1935		12.00
$ 5	1938		7.00
$10	1938		12.00

*THE EASTERN TOWNSHIPS BANK 1855 - 1912

$5 1906

Face: Train passing hay field

Back: Bank Crest

V.G. $150.00

THE EXCHANGE BANK OF TORONTO 1855

$1 1855

Face: Seated Indian, deer and counter

Back: Plain

$2 1855

Face: Men with cradles

Back: Plain

$5 1855

Face: Sailing ship

Back: Plain

$10 1855

Face: Steamers and sailing
ships
Back: Plain

Denom.	Issue Date	Buy Price V.G.
$ 1	1855	5.00
$ 2	1855	5.00
$ 5	1855	5.00
$10	1855	5.00

*THE FARMERS BANK OF CANADA 1906 - 1910

$5 1907-1908

Face: Farmer pumping
water for livestock
Back: Lathework, counters
and bank name

V.G. $1,000.00

THE FARMER'S JOINT STOCK BANKING CO. 1835 - 1849

$2 (10s) 1837

Face: Seated woman haying
in background
Back: Plain

V.G. $100.00

THE FARMERS BANK OF RUSTICO 1862 - 1892

$1 1872

Face: Ploughing with
horses
Back: Plain

V.G. $125.00

THE FARMERS BANK OF ST. JOHN'S 1837 - 1838

$1.25 1837

Face: Seated "Agriculture" figure, steamboat in background
Back: Plain
V.G. $500.00

THE FEDERAL BANK OF CANADA 1874 - 1888

$5 1874

Face: Workmen, ornate 5 and factories
Back: Lathework, counters and bank name
V.G. $100.00

*THE GORE BANK 1835 - 1870

$4 1836-1850

Face: Royal Crest
Back: Plain
V.G. $200.00

THE GORE BANK OF HAMILTON ca. 1837

$10 18--

Face: Seated female with plaque depicting lion
Back: Plain
V.G. $20.00

THE HALIFAX BANKING COMPANY 1825 - 1903

$20 1863, 1871

Face: Ship in Halifax
harbour
Back: Lathework, counters
and bank name

V.G. $1,250.00

*THE BANK OF HAMILTON 1872 - 1923

$5 1892

Face: "Agriculture" figure
Back: Head Office

$5 1909, 1914

Face: Seated Britannia,
Agriculture and
Commerce allegory
Back: Lathework, counters
and bank name

$10 1909, 1914

Face: Seated allegorical
female, Agriculture
and Commerce
allegory
Back: Lathework, counters
and bank name

$5 1922

Face: Seated Britannia,
Agriculture and
Commerce allegory
Back: Lathework, counters
and bank name

$25 1922

Face: Allegorical women
Back: Lathework, counters
and bank name

Denom.	Issue Date	Variety	Buy Price V.G.
$ 5	1892		75.00
$ 5	1914	Mss. signature, r.	20.00
$10	1914	Mss. signature, r.	40.00
$ 5	1922		20.00
$25	1922		60.00

HENRY'S BANK   1837

$1 1837

Face: Seated allegorical male
Back: Plain

V.G. $15.00

*BANQUE D'HOCHELAGA 1873 - 1925

$5 1914

Face: Place d'Arms
Back: Provincial Arms

V.G. $60.00

$10 1917

Face: Statue with four figures
Back: Provincial Arms

V.G. $60.00

*THE HOME BANK OF CANADA 1903 - 1923

$5 1904-1920

Face: Seated allegorical female, ships in background
Back: Three children reading

V.G. $250.00

*THE IMPERIAL BANK OF CANADA 1873 - 1961

$4 1875

Face: Ornate 4 over Royal
       Crest
Back: Lathework, counters
       and bank name

$5 1915-1920

Face: Royal Crest with
       ornate 5
Back: Lathework, counters
       and bank name

$10 1915-1920

Face: Bank Arms
Back: Lathework, counters
       and bank name

$20 1915-1920

Face: Farmer with horse-
       drawn mower
Back: Lathework, counters
       and bank name

$5 1923

Face: Howland - Phipps
Back: Lion over crown

$10 1923

Face: Howland - Phipps
Back: Lion over crown

134

$5 1934

Face: Phipps - Ralph
Back: Lion over crown

$10 1934

Face: Phipps - Ralph
Back: Lion over crown

$5 1939

Face: Jaffray - Phipps
Back: Lion over crown

$10 1939

Face: Jaffray - Phipps
Back: Lion over crown

Denom.	Issue Date	Variety	Buy Price V.G.
$ 4	1875	Mss. Howland signature, r.	250.00
$ 5	1916		40.00
$10	1920		30.00
$20	1915		75.00
$ 5	1923		15.00
$10	1923		15.00
$ 5	1934	Phipps signature, l.	7.00
$10	1934	Phipps signature, l.	11.00
$ 5	1939		8.00
$10	1939		12.00

THE INTERNATIONAL BANK OF CANADA
1858 - 1859

$1 1858

Face: Roebling Suspension
      Bridge
Back: Plain

$2 1858

Face: Royal Crest
Back: Plain

$5 1858

Face: Cattle drinking at
      river
Back: Plain

Denom.	Issue Date	Variety	Buy Price V.G.
$1	1858	Bridge; two signatures	10.00
$2	1858	Two signatures	5.00
$5	1858	One signature	5.00

*BANQUE INTERNATIONALE DU CANADA
1911 - 1913

$5 1911

Face: R. Forget
Back: Globe

V.G. $1,250.00

THE BANK OF LOWER CANADA Late 1830's

$3 18--

Face: Allegorical figures
Back: Plain

V.G. $50.00

Note: Various dates from
1839-1851 and all signatures
are of questionable
authenticity.

MACDONALD & CO. 1859 - 1866

$1 1863

Face: Royal Arms
Back: Plain

$5 1863

Face: Royal Arms
Back: Plain

$10 1863

Face: Royal Arms
Back: Plain

Denom.	Issue Date	Variety	Buy Price V.G.
$ 1	1863	Arm upraised	50.00
$ 5	1863	Arm down	50.00
$10	1863	Arm upraised	50.00

THE MARITIME BANK OF THE DOMINION
OF CANADA 1872 - 1887

$5 1881

Face: Dock scene
Back: Anchor, barrels and bale

V.G. $350.00

THE MECHANICS BANK 1865 - 1879

$4 1872

Face: Men working in
  carpenter's shop
Back: Lathework, counters
  and bank name

V.G. $30.00

$5 1872

Face: Farmer pumping
  water for livestock
Back: Lathework, counters
  and bank name

V.G. $25.00

*THE MERCHANTS BANK OF CANADA
1868 - 1923

$5 1900, 1903

Face: Sailing ships
Back: Gypsy woman

$10 1906, 1907

Face: Horse-drawn reaper
Back: Sailor with telescope

$5 1916

Face: Steamship
Back: Two beavers

$10 1916

Face: Horse-drawn reaper
Back: Sailor

$5 1917

Face: Men loading canoes
Back: Bank Crest

$10 1917

Face: Steamship, train at
dock
Back: Bank Crest

$20 1917

Face: Steer's head
Back: Bank Crest

$5 1919

Face: Prince of Wales
Back: Bank Crest

$10 1919
Face: Sir Hugh Allan
Back: Bank Crest

Denom.	Issue Date	Variety	Buy Price V.G.
$ 5	1900, 1903	Andrew Allan signature, r.	75.00
$10	1906, 1907		40.00
$ 5	1916		75.00
$10	1916		40.00
$ 5	1917	Mss. signature, r.	75.00
$10	1917	Mss. signature, r.	75.00
$20	1917	Mss. signature, l.	150.00
$ 5	1919		125.00
$10	1919		125.00

*THE METROPOLITAN BANK, Toronto
1902 - 1914

$5 1902

Face: Two seated women flanking standing child

Back: Royal Crest

V.G. $250.00

*THE MOLSONS BANK 1837 - 1925

$6 1871

Face: Two beavers
Back: Lathework, counters and bank name

$7 1871

Face: Men working on ship's hull
Back: Lathework, counters and bank name

$5 1903, 1904

Face: Ornate 5, woman, cherub

Back: Lathework, counters and bank name

$10 1905

Face: Indian and woman flanking ornate X

Back: Lathework, counters and bank name

$5 1908

Face: Macpherson - Molson

Back: Bank Crest

$10 1908

Face: Macpherson - Molson

Back: Bank Crest

$5 1912

Face: Wm. Molson

Back: Bank Crest

$10 1912

Face: Wm. Macpherson

Back: Bank Crest

$50 1914

Face: Wm. Molson
Back: Bank Crest

$10 1916

Face: River and town
Back: Bank Crest

$5 1922

Face: F.W. Molson
Back: Bank Crest

$10 1922

Face: Wm. Molson
Back: Bank Crest

Denom.	Issue Date	Variety	Buy Price V.G.
$ 6	1871		1,000.00
$ 7	1871		1,000.00
$ 5	1903, 1904		50.00
$10	1905		50.00
$ 5	1908		50.00
$10	1908		25.00
$ 5	1912		15.00
$10	1912		50.00
$50	1914		250.00
$10	1916		25.00
$ 5	1918	Design as 1908	30.00
$10	1918	Design as 1908	15.00
$ 5	1922		10.00
$10	1922		20.00

*THE BANK OF MONTREAL   1822 to date

$1 1846, 1849

Face: Ship in harbour
Back: Plain

$1 1852

Face: Bank Crest
Back: Plain

$1 1853-1857

Face: Bank Crest
Back: Lathework and
counters

$2 1856-1857

Face: Bank Crest
Back: Lathework and
counters

$4 1859

Face: Wellington
Back: St. George and
dragon

$5 1862

Face: Corner view of head
office building
Back: Plain

$4 1871

Face: Woman, cherubs and
       ornate 4
Back: Lathework, counters
      and bank name

$10 1882

Face: Cherubs and
      ornate X
Back: Lathework, counters
      and bank name

$20 1891

Face: Bank Crest
Back: Head office

$5 1895

Face: Counter and Bank
      Crest
Back: Toronto branch

$5 1904

Face: Bank Crest
Back: Head office

$10 1904

Face: Clouston - Smith
Back: Toronto branch

$20 1904

Face: Clouston -
    Drummond
Back: Head office

$5 1911

Face: Bank Crest
Back: Head office

$5 1912

Face: Bank Crest
Back: Head office

$10 1912

Face: Meredith - Smith
Back: Toronto branch

$5 1914

Face: Bank Crest
Back: Head office

$10 1914

Face: Williams-Taylor -
    Meredith
Back: Toronto branch

$5 1931
Face: Bank Crest
Back: Head office

$10 1931
Face: Dodds - Gordon
Back: Toronto branch

$5 1938
Face: Bank Crest
Back: Head office

$10 1938
Face: Spinney-Gordon
Back: Toronto branch

$5 1942
Face: Bank Crest
Back: Head office

Denom.	Issue Date	Variety	Buy Price V.G.
$ 1 (5s)	1846, 1849		200.00
$ 1 (5s)	1852		175.00
$ 1	1853-1857		200.00
$ 2	1856-1857		200.00

146

Denom.	Issue Date	Variety	Buy Price V.G.
$ 4	1859	Green St. George back	300.00
$ 5	1862		150.00
$ 4	1871		200.00
$10	1882		300.00
$20	1891		400.00
$ 5	1895		125.00
$ 5	1904		7.50
$10	1904		12.00
$20	1904		22.00
$ 5	1911		30.00
$ 5	1912		15.00
$10	1912		15.00
$ 5	1914	Mss. signature, l.	6.00
$10	1914	Mss. signature, l.	11.00
$ 5	1931	Large size note	6.00
$10	1931	Large size note	11.00
$ 5	1935	Small size note, design as 1931	6.00
$10	1935	Small size note, design as 1931	11.00
$ 5	1938		6.00
$10	1938		11.00
$ 5	1942		5.50

*LA BANQUE NATIONALE   1860 - 1925

$5 1897

Face: Train
Back: Arms of the City of
       Quebec

$10 1897

Face: Farmer ploughing
Back: Arms of the City of
       Quebec

$5 1922

Face: Monument
Back: Arms of the City of
Quebec

Denom.	Issue Date	Buy Price V.G.
$ 5	1897	75.00
$10	1897	75.00
$ 5	1922	75.00

*THE BANK OF NEW BRUNSWICK 1820 - 1913

$1 1860-1868

Face: Seated Britannia
flanked by women
and cherubs
Back: Cherubs, cask and
bale, twice

$5 1892

Face: Seated Britannia
flanked by women
and cherubs
Back: Bank building

$5 1904

Face: View of St. John
Back: Bank building

$10 1903

Face: Seated Britannia
flanked by women
and cherubs
Back: Bank building

Denom.	Issue Date	Buy Price V.G.
$ 1	1860-1868	175.00
$ 5	1892	200.00
$ 5	1904	250.00
$10	1903	300.00

THE NEW CASTLE DISTRICT LOAN COMPANY 1836

$4 (20s) 1836

Face: King William IV on
Royal Crest

Back: Plain

V.G. $50.00

*THE NIAGARA DISTRICT BANK   1853 - 1875

$5 (£1.5) 1862

Face: Three men studying
chart at dockside

Back: Plain

$5 1872

Face: Paddle wheel
steamer

Back: Lathework, counters
and bank name

$10 1872

Face: Niagara Falls

Back: Lathework, counters
and bank name

Denom.	Issue Date	Buy Price V.G.
$ 5 (£1.5)	1862	350.00
$ 5	1872	350.00
$10	1872	350.00

THE NIAGARA SUSPENSION BRIDGE BANK
1836 - 1841

$1 1836-1841

Face: Mythical Niagara
suspension bridge
Back: Lathework
or Plain

$3 1836-1841

Face: Mythical Niagara
suspension bridge
Back: Lathework
or Plain

$5 1836-1841

Face: Mythical Niagara
suspension bridge
Back: Lathework
or Plain

$10 1841

Face: Mythical Niagara
suspension bridge
Back: Plain

Denom.	Issue Date	Buy Price V.G.
$ 1 (5s)	1836-1841	5.00
$ 3 (15s)	1836-1841	10.00
$ 5 (25s)	1836-1841	10.00
$10	1841	10.00

*THE NORTHERN BANK 1905 - 1908

$10 1905

Face: Farmer cutting wheat
with binder
Back: Lathework, counters
and bank name

V.G. $750.00

*THE NORTHERN CROWN BANK   1908 - 1918

$5 1908, 1914

Face: Farmer and horses on prairies
Back: Floral emblems and crown

V.G. $400.00

*THE BANK OF NOVA SCOTIA   1832 to date

$4 1870-1877

Face: Beehive and flowers
Back: Lathework, counters and bank name

$5 1870-1877

Face: St. George slaying dragon
Back: Lathework, counters and bank name

$10 1877-1929

Face: Unicorn, shield and Indian
Back: Lathework, counters and bank name

$5 1898-1908

Face: Mining scene
Back: Bank Seal

$20 1903-1929

Face: Fishermen in small boat
Back: Bank Seal

151

$5 1918

Face: Archibald - Richardson
Back: Bank Seal

$5 1924

Face: Campbell - McLeod
Back: Bank Seal

$5 1929

Face: Moore - McLeod
Back: Bank Seal

$5 1935

Face: McLeod - Patterson
Back: Bank Seal

$10 1935

Face: Unicorn, shield and lion
Back: Bank Seal

152

Denom.	Issue Date	Buy Price V.G.
$ 4	1877	175.00
$ 5	1870-1877	200.00
$10	1924, 1929	11.00
$ 5	1908	20.00
$20	1929	22.00
$ 5	1918	20.00
$ 5	1924	7.00
$ 5	1929	6.00
$ 5	1935	6.00
$10	1935	11.00

*THE ONTARIO BANK   1857 - 1906

$4 1870

Face: Farmer ploughing
Back: Lathework, counters
and bank name

V.G. $125.00

$5 1888

Face: Indian brave
Back: Lathework, counters
and bank name

V.G. $350.00

*THE BANK OF OTTAWA 1874 - 1919

$5 1903

Face: Parliament Buildings
Back: Crest

V.G. $250.00

$10 1913

Face: Dairy farm scene
Back: Ottawa Crest

V.G. $250.00

*THE BANK OF THE PEOPLE   1835 - 1841

$8 (£2) 1840

Face: Royal Crest
Back: Plain

V.G. $1,500.00

*LA BANQUE DU PEUPLE   1835 - 1895

$4 (20s) 1847-1870

Face: Milkmaid and cows
Back: Portrait of young
woman in oval

V.G. $300.00

THE BANK OF PRINCE EDWARD ISLAND 1856 - 1881

$1 1872, 1877

Face: Woman cutting grain
with sickle
Back: Lathework, counters
and bank name

$2 1872, 1877

Face: Horse being watered
at stream
Back: Lathework, counters
and bank name

$5 1872, 1877

Face: Farmer watering
livestock at pump
Back: Lathework, counters
and bank name

154

$10 1872

Face: Fishermen and
sailing ships
Back: Lathework, counters
and bank name

$20 1872

Face: Woman, ship in dry-
dock
Back: Lathework, counters
and bank name

Denom.	Issue Date	Buy Price V.G.
$ 1	1877	35.00
$ 2	1877	35.00
$ 5	1877	50.00
$10	1872	40.00
$20	1872	40.00

*LA BANQUE PROVINCIALE DU CANADA
1900 - 1979

$5 1907

Face: Train in station
Back: Head office

$5 1913-1928

Face: Ornate V
Back: Head office

$5 1935

Face: S.J.B. Rolland
Back: Bank building

$10 1935

Face: S.J.B. Rolland
Back: Bank building

$5 1936

Face: Charles A. Roy
Back: Bank building

$10 1936

Face: Charles A. Roy
Back: Bank building

Denom.	Issue Date	Buy Price V.G.
$ 5	1907	200.00
$ 5	1928	10.00
$ 5	1935	6.00
$10	1935	11.00
$ 5	1936	10.00
$10	1936	15.00

*THE QUEBEC BANK 1818 - 1917

$5 1908

Face: Seated woman with
      lion
      (improved design)
Back: Bank Crest
  or Quebec City -
      Prescott Gate

$10 1908

Face: Docks at Quebec City
Back: Bank Crest
  or Quebec City -
      Hope Gate

$20 1911

Face: Cherub with winged
      wheel and power
      lines
Back: Bank Crest
  or Quebec City -
      PrescottGate

Denom.	Issue Date	Buy Price V.G.
$ 5	1908	125.00
$10	1908	125.00
$20	1911	200.00

*THE ROYAL BANK OF CANADA 1901 to date

$5 1901, 1909

Face: Seated woman with
      two children
Back: Royal Crest

$10 1901, 1909

Face: Seated allegorical
female
Back: Royal Crest

$20 1901, 1909

Face: Seated woman and
lion
Back: Royal Crest

$5 1913

Face: Canadian Coat-of-
Arms
Back: Royal Crest

$10 1913

Face: Battleship
Back: Royal Crest

$20 1913

Face: Train on prairies
Back: Royal Crest

$5 1927

Face: Coat-of-Arms
Back: Royal Crest

$10 1927

Face: Coat-of-Arms
Back: Royal Crest

$20 1927

Face: Coat-of-Arms
Back: Royal Crest

$5 1935

Face: Coat-of-Arms
Back: Royal Crest

$10 1935

Face: Coat-of-Arms
Back: Royal Crest

$5 1943

Face: Coat-of-Arms
Back: Royal Crest

Denom.	Issue Date	Variety	Buy Price V.G.
$ 5	1909	Green outlined 5's	25.00
$10	1909	Black frame	35.00
$20	1901		100.00
$ 5	1913	Mss. signature, l.	7.00
$10	1913	Mss. signature, l.	12.00

Denom.	Issue Date	Variety	Buy Price V.G.
$20	1913	Mss. signature, l.	22.00
$ 5	1927		6.00
$10	1927		11.00
$20	1927		22.00
$ 5	1935		6.00
$10	1935		11.00
$ 5	1943		30.00

*THE SOVEREIGN BANK OF CANADA 1901 - 1908

$5 1902-1905

Face: King Edward VII
Back: Bank Crest

V.G. $400.00

*THE STANDARD BANK OF CANADA 1876 - 1928

$5 1914-1919

Face: Allegorical woman
wearing wreath
Back: Bank Crest

$10 1914-1919

Face: W.F. Cowan
Back: Bank Crest

$20 1914-1919

Face: Two allegorical
women, one wearing
mantilla, the other
wearing wreath of
roses
Back: Bank Crest

$10 1924

Face: Seated Britannia
Back: Bank Crest

Denom.	Issue Date	Variety	Buy Price V.G.
$ 5	1919	Francis-Easson signatures	15.00
$10	1919	Francis-Easson signatures	20.00
$20	1919	Francis-Easson signatures	75.00
$10	1924	White signature, l.	25.00

*THE STERLING BANK OF CANADA 1905 - 1924

$10 1906

Face: Seated woman
holding flag
Back: Seated Britannia

$5 1914

Face: Train
Back: Princess Patricia of
Connaught

$10 1921

Face: Female with anchor
Back: Indian and woods-
man flanking counter

Denom.	Issue Date	Buy Price V.G.
$10	1906	125.00
$ 5	1914	125.00
$10	1921	175.00

*THE BANK OF TORONTO 1855 - 1954

$1 1856-1865

Face: Reclining farmer
Back: Engraved portraits of
      Queen Victoria and
      Prince Consort
  or Plain

$4 1876

Face: Allegorical female
      and two children
Back: Lathework and
      counter

$5 1887-1929

Face: Royal Crest
Back: Medallion engraved
      portraits of Queen
      Victoria and Prince
      Consort

$10 1887-1929

Face: Crest of Toronto
Back: Medallion engraved
      portraits of Queen
      Victoria and Prince
      Consort

$20 1887-1929

Face: Train
Back: Medallion engraved
      portraits of Queen
      Victoria and Prince
      Consort

$5 1935, 1937

Face: Royal Crest
Back: Medallion engraved
      portraits of Queen
      Victoria and Prince
      Consort

$10   1935, 1937

Face: Crest of Toronto
Back: Medallion engraved
portraits of Queen
Victoria and Prince
Consort

$20 1935, 1937

Face: Train
Back: Medallion engraved
portraits of Queen
Victoria and Prince
Consort

Denom.	Issue Date	Variety	Buy Price V.G.
$ 1	1859		200.00
$ 4	1876		400.00
$ 5	1917	Mss. signature, l.	15.00
$10	1929		20.00
$20	1923		22.00
$ 5	1935, 1937		6.00
$10	1935, 1937		11.00
$20	1935, 1937		22.00

THE UNION BANK   1838 - ca. 1840

$1 1838

Face: Posing female with
sculptures
Back: Plain
 or Lathework,
miniature
vignettes and
"STEEL PLATE"

$2 1838

Face: Seated Mercury, ship
in background
Back: Plain
 or Lathework,
miniature
vignettes and
"STEEL PLATE"

$5 1838

Face: Seated allegorical
female and Indian
Back: Plain
or Lathework,
miniature
vignettes and
"STEEL PLATE"

Denom.	Issue Date	Buy Price V.G.
$1	1838	25.00
$2	1838	25.00
$5	1838	25.00

*THE UNION BANK OF CANADA 1886 - 1925

$5 1903, 1907

Face: Farmers harvesting
with horses
Back: Bank Crest

$10 1903, 1907

Face: Cowboy roping steers
Back: Bank Crest

$5 1921

Face: Hamilton - Allan
Back: Lathework, counters
and bank name

$10 1921

Face: Hamilton - Allan
Back: Lathework, counters
and bank name

Denom.	Issue Date	Buy Price V.G.
$ 5	1907	35.00
$10	1903-1907	125.00
$ 5	1921	25.00
$10	1921	25.00

*THE UNION BANK OF LOWER CANADA
1865 - 1886

$1 1866

Face: Crest flanked by man with flag and Indian

Back: Lathework and bank name

V.G. **$350.00**

*UNION BANK OF NEWFOUNDLAND   1854 - 1894

£1 1865, 1867

Face: Sailing ship
Back: Plain

$2 1882

Face: James Smith
Back: Lathework, counters and bank name

$5 1889

Face: Cherub
Back: Cattle at pond

$10 1889

Face: Sailing ship
Back: Woman and strong box

Denom.	Issue Date	Buy Price V.G.
£ 1	1865, 1867	150.00
$ 2	1882	75.00
$ 5	1889	75.00
$10	1889	125.00

BANK OF UPPER CANADA, Kingston 1819 - 1822

$1 1819, 1820

Face: Steamboat, sheaf and plough
Back: Plain

$2 1819, 1820

Face: Seated "Justice" figure, barrels
Back: Plain

$5 1819-1822

Face: Fort, shipbuilding scene
Back: Plain

Denom.	Issue Date	Buy Price V.G.
$1	1820	6.00
$2	1820	10.00
$5	1819-1822	10.00

THE BANK OF UPPER CANADA, York 1821 - 1866

$1 1859, 1861

Face: St. George slaying dragon
Back: Lathework and counters

$2 1859, 1861

Face: Sailor reclining on
shore by anchor
Back: Lathework and
counters

$4 1859, 1861

Face: Two women and
Crest
Back: Lathework and
counters

$5 1859, 1861

Face: Two women and
Crest
Back: Lathework and
counters

Denom.	Issue Date	Variety	Buy Price V.G.
$1	1861	Engr. date, one signature	75.00
$2	1859	Engr. date, two signatures	75.00
$4	1859	Engr. date, two signatures	75.00
$5	1861	Engr. date, one signature	75.00

*THE BANK OF VANCOUVER 1910 - 1914

$20 1910

Face: Fishing at New
Westminster
Back: Parliament Buildings
at Victoria

V.G. $3,000.00

THE BANK OF WESTERN CANADA   1859 - 1863

$1 1859

Face: Royal Crest
Back: Plain

Buy Price ..... V.G. - $5.00

*THE WESTERN BANK OF CANADA   1882 - 1909

$5 1882

Face: Farm implements
and produce
Back: Lathework, counters
and bank name

V.G. $600.00

$10 1882

Face: Shepherdess with
lamb and ewe
Back: Lathework, counters
and bank name

V.G. $600.00

THE WESTMORELAND BANK OF NEW BRUNSWICK   1854 - 1867

$1 1854-1859

Face: Shipbuilding scene
Back: Plain

$2 1854-1859

Face: Train
Back: Plain

$4 1854-1859

Face: Farm family with
picnic basket
Back: Plain

$1 1861

Face: Shipbuilding scene
Back: Lathework

$2 1861

Face: Train
Back: Lathework

$5 1861

Face: Farm family with
picnic basket
Back: Lathework

Denom.	Issue Date	Variety	Buy Price V.G.
$1	1854-1859		5.00
$2	1854-1859		5.00
$4	1854-1859		10.00
$1	1861	Remainder, unsigned at left	3.00
$2	1861	Remainder, unsigned at left	3.00
$5	1861	Remainder, unsigned at left	3.00

*THE WEYBURN SECURITY BANK 1910 - 1931

$5 1911

Face: Train in city
Back: Lathework, counters
and bank name

V.G. $150.00

THE ZIMMERMAN BANK 1854 - 1859

$1 1856

Face: Roebling Suspension
Bridge
Back: Plain

$3 1856

Face: Roebling Suspension
Bridge
Back: Plain

$5 1856

Face: Roebling Suspension
Bridge
Back: Plain

$10 1856

Face: Prince Consort
Back: Plain

Denom.	Issue Date	Variety	Buy Price V.G.
$ 1	1856	Elgin, red ONE protector	25.00
$ 3	1856		25.00
$ 5	1856	Elgin, red FIVE protector	25.00
$10	1856		25.00

CANADIAN NOTE-ISSUING BANKS

The following list of banks identifies in alphabetical order all the non-government banks which issued (or ordered) Canadian notes. Each bank has been assigned a catalogue number. This number permits every note issud to be accurately identified and given its own specific number, a Charlton Number.

There are several types of banks:

Private Bank: A bank which operated without a charter, usually as a private partnership.

Chartered Bank: A bank which was incorporated by an act of parliament and sold stock to the general public.

Spurious or Phantom Bank: A bank which has no legal existence, whose name is found on notes intended to deceive the unwary. Such spurious notes were often made in some vague imitation of some legitimate bank's notes, frequently by using the colloquial name of such an institution.

Wildcat Bank: A bank with legal existence, but whose main purpose was to "push" its notes on the public, with no intention of redeeming most of them.

1. The Bank of Acadia, Liverpool, N.S. 1872-1873
2. The Accommodation Bank, Kingston, U.C. 1836-1837
    Spurious
3. The Agricultural Bank, Montreal, L.C. 1837
    Phantom
4. The Agricultural Bank, Toronto, U.C. 1834-1837
5. Arman's Bank, Montreal, L.C., 1837
6. *Barclay's Bank (Canada), Montreal, Que., 1929-1956
7. La Banque de Boucherville, Boucherville, L.C., 1830's
8. The Bank of Brantford, Brantford, C.W., 1857-1860's
9. The British Canadian Bank, Toronto, Ont., 1883-1884
10. *The Bank of British Columbia, Victoria, B.C., 1862-1901
11. *The Bank of British North America, 1836-1918
12. Canada Bank, Montreal, L.C., 1792
13. The Canada Bank, Toronto, C.W., 1855
14. The Bank of Canada, Montreal, L.C., 1813-1831
    (no relation to the present Bank of Canada)
15. *The Canadian Bank of Commerce, Toronto, Ont.,
    1867-1961
16. Banque Canadienne, St. Hyacinthe, L.C., 1836-1838
17. *Banque Canadienne Nationale, Montreal, Que.,
    1924-1979

18. The Central Bank of Canada, Toronto, Ont., 1883-1887
19. Central Bank of New Brunswick, Fredericton, N.B., 1834-1866
20. Charlotte County Bank, St. Andrew's, N.B., 1825-1865
21. Bank of Charlottetown, Charlottetown, P.E.I., 1852 Spurious
22. The City Bank, Montreal, L.C., 1833-1876
23. *City Bank, Saint John, N.B., 1836-1839
24. The Bank of Clifton, Clifton, C.W., 1859-1863 Wildcat
25. The Colonial Bank of Canada, Toronto, C.W., 1856-1863
26. The Colonial Bank of Chatham, Chatham, U.C., 1837-1839 Spurious
27. Commerical Bank, Brockville, U.C., 1837   Spurious
28. Commercial Bank, Kingston, U.C., 1837 Spurious
29. *The Commercial Bank of Canada, Kingston, C.W., 1856-1868
30. The Commercial Bank of Fort Erie, Fort Erie, U.C., 1836-1839   Spurious
31. The Commercial Bank of Lake Ontario, Niagara Falls, U.C., 1837
32. *The Commercial Bank of Manitoba, Winnipeg, Man., 1885-1893
33. *The Commercial Bank of the Midland District, Kingston, U.C., 1831-1856
34. Commercial Bank of Montreal, Montreal, L.C., 1835-1837
35. The Commercial Bank of New Brunswick, Saint John, N.B., 1834-1868
36. *Commercial Bank of Newfoundland, St. John's, Nfld., 1857-1894
37. *The Commercial Bank of Windsor, Windsor, N.S., 1864-1902
38. Commercial Branch Bank of Canada, Collingwood, C.W., 1861-1862   Phantom
39. The Consolidated Bank of Canada, Montreal, Que., 1876-1879
40. The Bank of the County of Elgin, St. Thomas, C.W., 1857-1862
41. *The Crown Bank of Canada, Toronto, Ont., 1904-1908
42. *The Dominion Bank, Toronto, Ont., 1869-1955
43. Eastern Bank of Canada, Saint John, N.B., 1928-1934
44. *The Eastern Townships Bank, Sherbrooke, C.E., 1855-1912

45. The Exchange Bank, Quebec, L.C., 1840's
46. The Exchange Bank of Canada, Montreal, Que., 1871-1883
47. The Exchange Bank of Canada, Windsor, Ont., 1860's
48. The Exchange Bank of Toronto, Toronto, C.W., 1855
49. *The Exchange Bank of Yarmouth, Yarmouth, N.S., 1867-1903
50. The Exchange Bank Company of Chippewa, Chippewa, U.C., 1837   Spurious
51. The Farmer's Bank, Toronto, U.C., 1840's   Spurious
52. *The Farmers Bank of Canada, Toronto, Ont., 1906-1910
53. The Farmers' Bank of Malden, Malden, U.C., 1840's
54. The Farmer's Joint Stock Banking Co., Toronto, U.C., 1835-1849   (turned Wildcat in the late 1840's)
55. The Farmers J.S. Banking Co., Toronto, U.C., 1830's Spurious
56. The Farmers Bank of Rustico, Rustico, P.E.I., 1862-1892
57. The Farmers Bank of St. John's, St. John's, L.C., 1837-1838
58. The Federal Bank of Canada, Toronto, Ont., 1874-1888
59. The Bank of Fredericton, Fredericton, N.B., 1836-1839
60. The Free Holders Bank of the Midland District, Bath, U.C., 1837
61. Goderich Bank, Goderich, U.C., 1834   Possibly Spurious
62. *The Gore Bank, Hamilton, U.C., 1835-1870
63. The Gore Bank of Hamilton, Hamilton, U.C., ca. 1837 Spurious
64. The Grenville County Bank, Prescott, C.W., 1856
65. *The Halifax Banking Company, Halifax, N.S., 1825-1903
66. The Hamilton Bank, Hamilton, L.C., 1835
67. *The Bank of Hamilton, Hamilton, Ont., 1872-1923
68. Hart's Bank, Three Rivers, L.C., 1835-1847
69. Henry's Bank, La Prairie and Montreal, L.C., 1837
70. *Banque d'Hochelaga, Montreal, Que., 1873-1925
71. *The Home Bank of Canada, Toronto, Ont., 1903-1923
72. The Bank of Hull, Hull, L.C., 1837
73. *The Imperial Bank of Canada, Toronto, Ont., 1873-1961
74. The International Bank of Canada, Toronto, U.C. 1858-1859   (turned Wildcat in the late 1850's)
75. *Banque Internationale du Canada, Montreal, Que., 1911-1913
76. La Banque Jacques Cartier, Montreal, C.E., 1861-1900
77. The Kingston Bank, Kingston, L.C., 1837 Possibly Phantom

78. The Bank of Liverpool, Liverpool, N.S., 1871-1879
79. The Bank of London in Canada, London, Ont., 1883-1888
80. Lower Canada Bank, Montreal, L.C., 1837   Phantom
81. The Bank of Lower Canada, Quebec, L.C., late 1830's
82. Macdonald & Co., Victoria, B.C. 1859-1866
83. The Maritime Bank of the Dominion of Canada, Saint John, N.B., 1872-1887
84. The Mechanics Bank, Montreal, L.C., 1837   Spurious
85. The Mechanics Bank, Montreal, C.E., 1865-1879
86. The Mechanics Bank of Saint John's, Saint John's, L.C., 1837   Spurious
87. The Merchantile Banking Corporation, Halifax, N.S., 1878
88. *The Merchants Bank, Montreal, C.E., 1864-1868
89. The Merchants Bank, Toronto, U.C., 1837   Spurious
90. *The Merchants Bank of Canada, Montreal, Que., 1868-1923
91. *The Merchants Bank of Halifax, Halifax, N.S., 1864-1901
92. *The Merchants Bank of Prince Edward Island, Charlottetown, P.E.I., 1871-1906
93. The Merchants Exchange Bank, Goderich, C.W., 1853
94. The Metropolitan Bank, Montreal, Que., 1871-1876
95. The Metropolitan Bank, Toronto, Ont., 1902-1914
96. *The Molsons Bank, Montreal, C.E., 1837-1925
97. *Montreal Bank, Montreal, L.C., 1817-1822
98. The Montreal Bank, Montreal, C.W., 1840's-1850's Phantom
99. *The Bank of Montreal, Montreal, L.C., 1822 to date
100. *La Banque Nationale, Montreal, C.E., 1860-1925
101. *The Bank of New Brunswick, Saint John, N.B., 1820-1913
102. The Newcastle Banking Co., Amherst, U.C., 1836
103. The New Castle District Loan Company, Peterborough, U.C., 1836
104. *The Niagara District Bank, St. Catharines, C.W., 1853-1875
105. The Niagara Suspension Bridge Bank, Queenston, U.C., 1836-1841
106. *The Northern Bank, Winnipeg, Man., 1905-1908
107. *The Northern Crown Bank, Winnipeg, Man., 1908-1918
108. *The Bank of Nova Scotia, Halifax, N.S., 1832 to date
109. *The Ontario Bank, Bowmanville, C.W., 1857-1906
110. The Bank of Ottawa, Montreal, L.C., 1837   Spurious

111. The Bank of Ottawa, Ottawa, Ont., 1874-1919
112. *The Bank of the People, Toronto, U.C., 1835-1841
113. *La Banque du Peuple, Montreal, L.C., 1835-1895
114. *The People's Bank of Halifax, Halifax, N.S., 1864-1905
115. *The People's Bank of New Brunswick, Fredericton, N.B., 1864-1907
116. The Phenix Bank, Phillipsburg, L.C., 1837-1841
     Possibly Spurious
117. The Pictou Bank, Pictou, N.S., 1873-1887
118. The Bank of Prince Edward Island, Charlottetown, P.E.I., 1856-1881
119. The Provincial Bank, London, Ont., 1884
120. The Provincial Bank of Canada, Stanstead, Ont., 1856-1863
121. *La Banque Provinciale du Canada, Montreal, Que., 1900-1979
122. *The Quebec Bank, Quebec, L.C., 1818-1917
123. Bank of Quebec Lower Canada, Quebec, L.C., 1841
     Phantom
124. *The Royal Bank of Canada, Montreal, Que. 1901 to date
125. The Royal Canadian Bank, Toronto, C.W., 1864-1876
126. The Saint Francis Bank, Stanstead, C.E., 1855
127. *La Banque de St. Hyacinthe, St. Hyacinthe, Que., 1873-1908
128. *La Banque de St. Jean, St. Jean, Que., 1873-1908
129. Banque St. Jean Baptiste, Montreal, Que., 1875
130. *The St. Lawrence Bank, Toronto, Ont., 1872-1876
131. The St. Lawrence Bank & Lumber Co., Malbaie, L.C., 1837   Spurious
132. *The St. Stephen's Bank, St. Stephen, N.B., 1836-1910
133. The Bank of Saskatchewan, Moose Jaw, Sask., 1913
134. *The Sovereign Bank of Canada, Montreal, Que., 1901-1908
135. The Stadacona Bank, Quebec City, Que., 1872-1879
136. *The Standard Bank of Canada, Toronto, Ont., 1876-1928
137. *The Sterling Bank of Canada, Toronto, Ont., 1905-1924
138. *The Summerside Bank, Summerside, P.E.I., 1866-1901
139. Tattersall Bank, Montreal, L.C., 183–
140. *The Bank of Toronto, Toronto, Ont., 1855-1954
141. *The Traders Bank of Canada, Toronto, Ont., 1885-1912
142. The Union Bank, Montreal, L.C., 1838-ca. 1840
143. *The Union Bank of Canada, Quebec City, Que., 1886-1925

COINS OF THE UNITED STATES

MINT MARKS

The United States decimal coinage is identified by the following mint marks:

C - Charlotte, North Carolina
CC - Carson City, Nevada
D - Dahlonega, Georgia (gold coins only)
D - Denver, Colorado (1906 to date)
O - New Orleans, Louisiana
S - San Francisco, California
P - Philadelphia, Pennsylvania

COPPER AND SILVER COINS

HALF CENTS: The United States half-cent was issued first in 1793. Issue continued until 1857, although there were various intervals when the coins were not struck. There were several major series of the coins, many of which had minor varieties. Generally, the coins are scarce and command a good premium.

Liberty Cap

Date	V.G.
1793	200.00
1794	60.00
1795	60.00
1796	500.00
1797	55.00

Draped Bust

Date	V.G.
1800	10.00
1802	70.00
1803	10.00
1804	10.00
1805	10.00
1806	10.00
1807	10.00
1808	10.00

Classic Head

Date	V.G.
1809	10.00
1810	10.00
1811	30.00
1825	10.00

Date	V.G.
1826	9.00
1828	9.00
1829	9.00
1831 Proof	450.00
1832	9.00
1833	9.00
1834	9.00
1835	9.00
1836 Proof	325.00

Matron Head

Date	V.G.
1840 Proof	325.00

Date	V.G.
1841 Proof	325.00
1842 Proof	325.00
1843 Proof	325.00
1844 Proof	325.00
1845 Proof	325.00
1846 Proof	325.00
1847 Proof	325.00
1848 Proof	325.00
1849	10.00
1850	10.00
1851	9.00
1852 Proof	325.00
1853	9.00
1855	9.00
1856	9.00
1857	10.00

LARGE CENTS: The large cents were issued every year from 1793 to 1857, except 1815. The coins were fashioned in copper and wore poorly. Specimens in good condition are rare and quite valuable. Like the half-cents, the large cents were struck at the Philadelphia Mint and had no mint mark.

Liberty Cap

Date	V.G.
1797	12.00
1798	12.00
*1799	250.00
1800	10.00
1801	10.00
1802-1803	10.00
**1804 Original	200.00
1805	10.00
1806	15.00
1807	10.00

Date	V.G.
1793	200.00
1794	25.00
1795	25.00
1796	25.00

*Beware of altered date, 9 over 8.
**Beware of restrike from a defective die.

Classic Head

Date	V.G.
1808	10.00
1809	50.00
1810	10.00
1811	30.00
1812	12.00
1813	20.00
1814	12.00

Draped Bust

Matron Head

Date	V.G.
1816-1817	3.00
1818-1820	3.00
1821	10.00
1822	3.00
1823	20.00
1824-1830	4.00
1831-1838	3.00
1839	4.00
1840-1843	2.75
1844-1856	2.50
1857	12.00

SMALL CENTS: The authorization act for the small cent was not passed until 1857, which means the 1856 Flying Eagle cents were patterns and not a commercial issue. Like all other series of United States cents struck before 1908, the Flying Eagle cents were minted at Philadelphia. In 1864 the one-cent piece was changed from a copper-nickel composition to a copper-tin-zinc alloy, and the weight was reduced. In 1909 the obverse design for the cent was changed to a bust of Lincoln. The use of this portrait continues although the reverse was changed in 1959 from the earlier wheat ears pattern to the Lincoln Memorial pattern.

Flying Eagle

Copper-Nickel - 1859-1864
Bronze - 1864-1909

Date	V.G.
*1856	400.00
1857	3.50
1858	3.50

*Beware of fake 1856's made by altering an 1858.

Indian Head Cents

Date		V.G.
1859		2.25
1860		2.00
1861		4.50
1862		1.50
1863		1.50
1864	Copper-Nickel	3.50
1864	Bronze	1.25
1865		1.25
1866		9.00
1867-1868		9.00
1869		15.00
1870		12.00
1871		15.00
1872		20.00
1873		3.50
1874		3.50
1875		3.50
1876		6.00

Date	V.G.
1877	100.00
1878	6.00
1879	1.50
1880	.85
1881-1883	.85
1884	1.00
1885	2.00
1886	1.00
1887-1893	.45
1894	1.00
1895-1899	.35
1900-1908	.30
*1908S	9.00
1909	.40
1909S	40.00

*Mint mark under wreath on reverse side.

Lincoln Head Cents

Date	V.G.
1909	.09
1909VDB	.60
1909S	15.00
1909SVDB	90.00
1910S	2.75
1911D	1.25

Date	V.G.
1911S	4.50
1912	.10
1912D	1.25
1912S	3.50
1913D	.70
1913S	2.50
*1914D	30.00
1914S	3.00
1915	.25
1915D	.25
1915S	2.75
1916S-1921S	.25
1922D	1.50
1923S	.65
1924D	4.00
1924S	.25
1925S & 1925D	.10
1926S	1.25
1927S	.15
1931D	1.25
1931S	13.00
1932	.40
1932D	.25
1933	.20
1933D	.75
1938S	.10
1939S	.03
1939D	.10
1955S	.10
1955 Double struck date	75.00

*Beware of altered date. No VDB on genuine 1914D cent.

TWO CENTS: The two-cent pieces were minted at Philadelphia from an alloy of 95% copper and 5% tin and zinc. Even though it was the first coin to bear the motto "In God We Trust," it was never a popular coinage. In the 1864 issue there were large and small motto varieties.

Date	V.G.
1864-1865	2.50
1866	2.50
1867	2.50
1868-1869	2.50
1870	3.00
1871	3.50
1872	25.00
1873 Proof	300.00

THREE CENTS: There were two types of three-cent coins minted, one was silver, the other nickel. The silver coins were minted from 1851 through 1873. In 1853 the fineness of the silver was raised from .750 to .900. Most of the pieces coined in the decade 1863-1873 were either exported or melted, and as a result they are now quite rare.

The nickel coins had a composition of 75% copper and 25% nickel. They were coined during the years 1865-1889.

Silver   Nickel

Date	V.G.	Date	V.G.
1851	5.00	1865-1870	2.50
1851O	8.00	1871-1872	2.50
1852-1853	5.00	1873	2.50
1854	8.00	1874	2.50
1855	10.00	1875-1876	3.50
1856	6.00	1877 Proof	350.00
1857	6.00	1878 Proof	150.00
1858	6.00	1879-1880	20.00
1859-1860	6.00	1881	2.50
1861-1862	6.00	1882-1883	10.00
1863 Proof	200.00	1884	15.00
1864 Proof	200.00	1885	20.00
1865 Proof	200.00	1886 Proof	100.00
1866-1872 Proof	200.00	1887	20.00
1873 Proof	225.00	1888-1889	15.00

HALF DIMES: The early pieces were struck in .892 fine silver. In 1837 the fineness was raised to .900. All coins of this denomination were minted at Philadelphia until 1838 when the New Orleans Mint and 1863 when the San Francisco Mint also began striking them. The half-dime was the first authorized coin of the United States. The first issue for circulation was struck in 1795 but dated 1794.

Flowing Hair

Date	V.G.
1794	200.00
1795	150.00

Draped Bust

Date	V.G.
1796	250.00
1797	175.00
1800	125.00
1801	125.00
1802	Rare
1803	125.00
1805	225.00

Capped Bust

Date	V.G.
1829	12.00
1830-1837	9.00

Liberty Seated

Date	V.G.
1838	3.50
1838O	30.00
1839O	4.00
1840	3.50
1840O	3.50
1841	3.50
1841O	5.00
1842	3.50
1842O	5.00
1843	3.50
1844	3.50
1844O	7.00
1845	3.50
1846	35.00
1847	3.50
1848	3.50
1848O	5.00

Date	V.G.
1849	3.50
1849O	12.50
1850	3.50
1850O	4.00
1851	3.50
1851O	5.00
1852	3.50
1852O	5.00
1853 Arrows	3.25
1853 No Arrows	7.00
1853O Arrows	3.25
1853O No Arrows	50.00
1854 Arrows	3.25
1854O Arrows	4.00
1855 Arrows	3.25
1855O Arrows	6.00
1856	3.25
1856O	4.00
1857	3.25
1857O	4.00
1858	3.25
1858O	4.00
1859 & 1859O	7.00
1860	3.25
1860O	3.00
1861	3.00
1862	3.00
1863	25.00
1863S	8.00
1864	75.00
1864S	12.00
1865	35.00
1865S	8.00
1866	35.00
1866S	7.00
1867	50.00
1867S	7.00
1868	12.00
1868S	4.50
1869	4.00
1869S	4.50
1870	3.50
1871	4.00
1871S	8.00
1872	4.00
1872S	4.00
1873	4.00
1873S	4.00

FIVE CENTS NICKEL: Until 1912 all five-cent nickel pieces were struck at Philadelphia. The composition of both the Shield and Liberty Head types was 75% copper and 25% nickel. This coinage was introduced to replace the silver half-dimes and fractional currency.

In 1912 San Francisco and Denver began minting Liberty Head five-cent pieces. But why the 1913 Liberty Head nickels were struck was never completely explained. These were not a regular issue and only five are known.

From 1913 to 1938 the Buffalo type nickel designed by J.E. Fraser was minted. Since 1938 the Jefferson nickel designed by F. Schlag has been struck.

Shield

Date	V.G.
1866	6.00
1867	4.00
1868	4.00
1869	4.00
1870	4.25
1871	15.00
1872	4.25
1873	4.25
1874	4.50
1875	6.00
1876	6.00
1877 Proof	500.00
1878 Proof	200.00
1879	30.00
1880	35.00
1881	30.00
1882	4.00
1883	4.00

Liberty Head

Date	V.G.
1883 No "CENTS"	1.00
1883 "CENTS"	2.50
1884	2.75
1885	60.00
1886	18.00
1887	2.25
1888	3.00
1889	2.00
1890	2.25
1891-1893	1.75
1894	2.50
1895-1896	1.50
1897-1898	.50
1899-1912	.15
1912D	.50
1912S	15.00
*1913	

*Only five known. None ever in circulation.

Indian Head or Buffalo Type

Date	V.G.
1913 Variety 1	1.00
1913D Variety 1	2.50
1913S Variety 1	4.00

Date	V.G.
1913 Variety 2	1.75
1913D Variety 2	15.00
1913S Variety 2	25.00
1914	2.00
1914D	10.00
1914S	2.50
1915	.90
1915D	3.00
1915S	5.00
1916D	2.50
1916S	1.75
1917D & 1917S	2.50
1918D & 1918S	2.50
1919D	2.50
1919S	2.00
1921S	7.50
1923S	1.25
1924S	3.00
1924D	1.25
1925D	2.50
1925S	2.00
1926D	1.75
1926S	4.00
1927D	.75
1927S	.85
1931S	2.00
Other Buffalo Types	.10

Jefferson Type

Date		V.G.
1938D		.40
1938S		1.00
1939D		1.50
1939S		.20
1950D	E.F. -	4.00

DIMES: The early dimes were struck in .892 fine silver, and all the earliest issues are now rare. The fineness was later raised to .900.

The 1894S Liberty Head dime was a very rare issue. Only 24 specimens were struck and like a number of other extremely rare United States coins, no current market price is quoted here.

The Mercury Head series introduced in 1916 was popular with many collectors, and the design was actually a representation of Liberty and not Mercury. The wings were intended to represent liberty of thought.

Draped Bust

Date	V.G.
1796	250.00
1797	200.00
1798 & 1800	100.00
1801	100.00
1802	125.00
1803	100.00
1804	175.00
1805 & 1807	100.00

Capped Bust

Date	V.G.
1809	40.00
1811	21.00
1814	15.00
1820	15.00
1821	15.00
1822	40.00
1823	15.00
1824	20.00
1825	15.00
1827	14.00
1828	15.00
1829	12.00
1830-1836	12.00
1837	12.00

Liberty Seated

Date	V.G.
1838	5.00
1838O	35.00
1839	4.50
1839O	5.00
1840	4.00
1840O	5.00
1841 Drapery	4.00
1841O	4.50
1842	3.25
1842O	3.50
1843	3.25
1843O	15.00
1844	15.00
1845	3.25
1845O	10.00

Date	V.G.
1846	25.00
1847	8.00
1848	3.50
1849	3.25
1849O	8.00
1850-1851	3.25
1850O	5.00
1851O	5.00
1852	3.25
1852O	5.00
1853 Arrows	4.00
1853O Arrows	4.50
1853 No Arrows	15.00
1854 Arrows	4.00
1854O	4.25
1855 Arrows	3.75
1856	3.25
1856O	3.50
1856S	25.00
1857O	3.25
1857-1858	3.25
1858O	3.00
1858S	15.00
1859-1859O	3.00
1859S	15.00
1860	3.00
1860O	150.00
1860S	7.00
1861S	12.00
1861	3.00
1862	3.00
1862S	7.00
1863	25.00
1863S	10.00
1864	25.00
1864S	7.50
1865	30.00
1865S	7.00
1866	35.00
1866S	7.50
1867	50.00
1867S	7.50
1868	5.00
1868S	6.00
1869S	6.00
1869-1870	3.00
1870S	30.00
1871CC	125.00

Date	V.G.	Date	V.G.
1871S	7.00	1893S	4.00
1871-1872	3.00	1894	3.50
1872CC	75.00	1894O	15.00
1872S	8.00	1895	20.00
1873 No Arrows	3.00	1895O	35.00
1873 Arrows	7.00	1895S	7.00
1873CC Arrows	250.00	1896	3.00
1873S	11.00	1896O	20.00
1874	6.00	1896S	18.00
1874CC	100.00	1897	1.00
1874S	11.00	1897O	15.00
1875-1877	2.50	1897S	4.00
1878	2.50	1898	1.00
1878CC	10.00	1898O	2.50
1879	22.00	1898S	2.50
1880	20.00	1899	1.00
1881	20.00	1899O	2.50
1882-1884	2.50	1899S	2.50
1884S	7.50	1900	1.00
1885S	40.00	1900O	2.50
1885-1886	2.50	1900S	1.25
1886S	7.50	1901O	1.25
1887	2.50	1901S	15.00
1887S	2.50	1902O	1.00
1888	2.50	1902S	2.50
1888S	2.50	1903O	1.00
1889	2.50	1903S	12.00
1889S	7.00	1904S	8.00
1890-1891 All Mints	2.50	1905O	1.00
		1905S	1.00
		1906D	1.00
		1906O	2.00
		1906S	1.00
		1907D, 1907O, 1907S	1.00
		1908-1908D	1.00
		1908O	1.50
		1908S	1.00
		1909-1910	1.00
		1909D-1909S	2.50
		1909O	1.25
		1910D	1.00
		1910S	1.50
		1911-1911D	1.00
		1911S-1912S	1.00
		1913S	6.00
		1914S	1.00
		1915-1916	1.00
		1915S	1.25

Liberty Head

Date	V.G.
1892	1.50
1892O	3.00
1892S	12.00
1893	2.50
1893O	5.00

Mercury Head

Date	V.G.
1916D	125.00
1917D	1.50
1919D	1.25
1919S	1.25
1921	12.00
1921D	15.00
1923S	1.00
1925D	1.50
1926S	4.00

1927D	1.00
1927S	1.00
1931	1.00
1931D	3.50
1931S	1.25

Roosevelt

Date	V.G.
1949S	1.00
1951S-1953	.75
1954S-1955S	.75
1955-1955D	.75

Common Dimes

Date	V.G.
1964 and earlier	.75

TWENTY CENTS: The 20-cent pieces were issued for only four years, 1875-1878. It was an unpopular coinage because it was confused with the 25-cent piece. The 1876CC strikes, most of which were melted, and the 1877 and 1878 strikes are rare.

Date	V.G.
1875	25.00
1875CC	25.00
1875S	25.00
1876	30.00
1877 Proof	800.00
1878 Proof	750.00

QUARTER DOLLARS: Quarters were struck first in .892 fine silver and later in .900 fine silver. They were authorized as issue in 1792 and first released in 1796.

The Liberty Standing type of 1916-1930 were prone to heavy wear, especially the date and pedestal on which it appeared. If a premium is to be paid, then the date must show. The Washington series of quarters (1932 to date) have small premiums generally, and in worn condition they are worth only their bullion value.

Draped Bust

Date	V.G.
1796	900.00
1804	125.00
1805	60.00
1806-1807	55.00

Capped Bust

Date	V.G.
1815	20.00
1818-1819	20.00
1820-1821	20.00
1822	20.00
1823	500.00
1824	25.00
1825	18.00
1828	18.00
1831-1838	18.00

Liberty Seated

Date	V.G.
1838-1839	7.00
1840	7.00
1840O	7.00
1841	10.00
1841O	6.00
1842	5.50
1843-1849	4.50
1849O	90.00
1850	4.50
1851-1852	4.50
1851O	50.00
1852O	90.00
1853 Arrows	6.00
1853O Arrows	7.00
1854-1854O-1855	5.00
1855O	30.00
1855S	30.00
1856-1856O	4.50
1856S	15.00
1857-1857O	4.50
1857S	20.00
1858-1858O	4.50
1858S	18.00
1859-1859O	4.50
1859S	20.00
1860-1861	4.50
1860O	4.50
1860S	20.00
1861-1862	4.50
1861S	15.00
1862S	15.00
1863	6.00
1864	12.00
1864S	55.00
1865	15.00
1865S	17.00
1866	25.00
1866S	20.00
1867	22.00
1867S	15.00
1868	14.00
1868S	14.00
1869	25.00
1869S	14.00
1870	12.00
1870CC	125.00
1871	4.50
1871S	20.00

Date	V.G.
1872	4.00
1872CC	100.00
1872S	15.00
1873 No Arrows	4.00
1873-1873S Arrows	12.00
1873CC Arrows	250.00
1874 Arrows	12.00
1874S Arrows	13.00
1875	4.50
1875S	6.00
1875CC	12.00
1876-1878 All Mints	4.50
1878S	75.00
1878CC	5.00
1879-1883	25.00
1884	30.00
1885	25.00
1886	35.00
1887-1888	30.00
1888S	4.50
1889	30.00
1890	17.00
1891	4.50
1891O	55.00
1891S	5.00

Liberty Head

Date	V.G.
1892	2.50
1892O	3.25
1892S	8.00
1893	2.50
1893O	3.00
1893S	4.50
1894	2.50
1894O-1894S	2.50
1895O	2.50
1895S	3.50

Date	V.G.
1896-1899	2.50
1896O	3.50
1896S	75.00
1897O	4.00
1897S	7.50
1898O	2.75
1898S	3.50
1899O	2.50
1899S	6.00
1900O	4.00
1900S	2.50
1901O	8.00
1901S	250.00
1902O	2.50
1902S	4.50
1903O	2.50
1903S	4.50
1904O	4.00
1905O	4.50
1905S	2.50
1906O	2.50
1907D	2.50
1907S	2.50
1908S	5.00
1909O	8.00
1909S-1910D	2.50
1911D-1911S	2.50
1912S	2.50
1913	6.00
1913D	2.50
1913S	100.00
1914S	8.00
1915S	2.50

Standing Liberty

Date	V.G.
1916	225.00
1917	4.00

189

Washington

Date	V.G.
1917S	4.50
1917D	4.50
1918-1918S	3.50
1918D	6.00
1919	6.00
1919D	18.00
1919S	22.00
1920	3.00
1920D	8.00
1920S	5.50
1921	20.00
1923-1924	3.00
*1923S	30.00
1924D	8.00
1924S	6.00
1926S	2.00
1927S	3.50
1927D	2.50

*Beware of altered date.

Date	V.G.
1932D	25.00
1932S	25.00
1937S	4.00

Common Quarters

Date	V.G.
1964 and earlier	2.50

HALF DOLLARS: The half dollar coinage was issued in .892 fine silver from 1794 until 1837 when the fineness was raised to .900. Like the half dime, the half dollar was authorized in 1792.

The 1964 Kennedy half dollars were struck in .900 fine silver, but the 1965-1970 issues were clad coins. The core of the clad coins was 21% silver and the outer layer 80% silver. In 1971 a shift was made to a copper core with a nickel-copper outer layer.

Flowing Hair

Date	V.G.
1794	225.00
1795	175.00

Draped Bust

Date	V.G.
1796	1,800.00
1797	1,800.00

190

Date	V.G.
1801	75.00
1802	70.00
1803	40.00
1805-1806	30.00
1807	20.00

Capped Bust

Date	V.G.
1808-1814	12.00
1815	100.00
1817-1819	10.00
1820	12.00
1821-1836	10.00
1837	15.00
1838	15.00
1839	15.00
1839O	40.00

Liberty Seated

Date	V.G.
1839	15.00
1840	7.00

Date	V.G.
1840O	7.00
1841	9.00
1841O	7.00
1842-1849 All Mints	7.00
1850	20.00
1850O	7.00
1851	20.00
1851O	7.00
1852	30.00
1852O	20.00
1853 All Mints	10.00
1854-1854O	8.00
1855-1855O	8.00
1855S	35.00
1856-1856O	6.00
1856S	9.00
1857-1857O	6.00
1857S	12.00
1858-1858O	5.00
1858S	8.00
1859-1859O	5.00
1859S	8.00
1860-1865	6.00
1866S No Motto	30.00
1866S Motto "In God We Trust"	6.00
1866, 1867, 1868	6.00
1867S-1868S	6.00
1869-1869S	6.00
1870-1870S	6.00
1870CC	100.00
1871	6.00
1871CC	30.00
1871S-1872	6.00
1872CC	25.00
1872S	6.00
1873 No Arrows	6.00
1873 Arrows	15.00
1873CC No Arrows	35.00
1873CC Arrows	25.00
1873S	22.00
1874	13.00
1874CC	35.00
1875-1875S	6.00
1875CC	6.00
1876	6.00
1876CC	6.00

Date	V.G.
1876S-1877	6.00
1877CC	7.00
1877S-1878	6.00
1878CC	75.00
1878S	700.00
1879	50.00
1880	50.00
1881	50.00
1882-1887	50.00
1888-1890	45.00
1891	6.00

Date	V.G.
1904O	5.00
1904S	8.00
1905	5.00
1905O	7.00
1913	8.00
1913S	5.00
1914	13.00
1915	12.00

Liberty Head

Liberty Walking

Date	V.G.
1892	6.00
1892O	45.00
1892S	40.00
1893O	10.00
1893-1894	6.00
1894O	6.00
1895O	6.00
1895 & 1897	5.00
1895S	10.00
1896O	10.00
1896S	30.00
1897O	25.00
1897S	30.00
1898O	7.00
1898S	5.00
1899O	5.00
1899S	6.00
1901O	5.00
1901S	8.00
1902S	5.00
1903S	5.00

Date	V.G.
1916	9.00
1916D On Obverse	5.00
1916S On Obverse	15.00
1917	5.00
1917D On Obverse	5.00
1917D On Reverse	5.00
1917S On Obverse	5.00
1917S On Reverse	5.00
1918	5.00
1921	25.00
1921D	40.00
1938D	13.00

Franklin

Franklin		Kennedy	
Date	V.G.	Date	V.G.
1948-1963	5.00	1964 Silver	5.00
		1965-1970	2.00

DOLLARS: The first issue of United States dollars was in 1794, and until 1804 the value was struck on the edge. The fineness was .8924 and the weight was 26.957 grams.

The 1804 silver dollar is one of the most publicized items in American numismatics. There were two reverses for the 1804 dollars, with eight specimens of the first type and seven of the second.

In 1837 the fineness was increased to .900 and the weight was reduced to 26.73 grams. After 1935 silver dollars were no longer minted for circulation. Collectors' coins have been struck in 40% silver, such as the Eisenhower dollars of 1971-1978. The circulation issue of the Eisenhower series was struck in a copper-nickel mixture.

Flowing Hair

Date	V.G.
1794	2,500.00
1795	250.00

Draped Bust

Liberty Seated

Date	V.G.
1840-1847	40.00
1848	50.00
1849	40.00
1850	50.00
1850O	40.00
1853	40.00
1854-1855	50.00
1856	45.00
1857	45.00
1858 Proof	Rare
1859	40.00

Date	V.G.
1796	200.00
1797	200.00
1798	200.00
1799-1803	150.00

Date	V.G.
1859O	40.00
1859S	55.00
1860	40.00
1860O	40.00
1861	50.00
1862-1865	50.00
1866	40.00
1867	40.00
1868-1870	35.00
1870CC	60.00
1871	35.00
1871CC	250.00
1872	35.00
1872S	60.00
1872CC	125.00
1873	35.00
1873CC	300.00

Date	V.G.
1889S	12.00
1890CC	10.00
1891CC	11.00
1892CC	20.00
1892S	12.00
1893	15.00
1893O	30.00
1893S	500.00
1893CC	35.00
1894	125.00
1894S	12.00
1894O	10.00
1895O	35.00
1895S	60.00
1896S	12.00
1898O	10.00
1902O	10.00
1903O	35.00
1903S	12.00
1904O	10.00

Liberty Head

Peace

Date	V.G.
1878	10.00
1879CC	30.00
1880CC	20.00
1881CC	35.00
1884CC	12.00
1885CC	40.00
1885S	10.00
1889S	12.00
1889CC	90.00

Date	V.G.
1921	12.00
1927	11.00
1927D	10.00
1928 No Mint Mark	75.00
1834S	12.00
1935S	10.00

194

TRADE DOLLARS: The trade dollars were coined in .900 fine silver weighing 27.216 grams, unlike the regular dollar which weighed 26.73 grams. The trade dollar was intended for circulation in the Orient, and it was issued from 1873 through 1885. The 1879-1885 issues were rare since only proof items for collecting were struck in those years. In 1887 a law was passed authorizing the Treasury of the United States to redeem all unmutilated trade dollars.

Date	V.G.
1874S	35.00
1874CC	35.00
1875	45.00
1875CC	35.00
1875S	35.00
1876-1876S	35.00
1876CC	35.00
1877-1877S	35.00
1877CC	35.00
1878 Proof	800.00
1878CC	100.00
1878S	35.00
1879 Proof	800.00
1880 Proof	800.00
1881 Proof	800.00
1882 Proof	800.00
1883 Proof	800.00

Date	V.G.
1874	35.00
1873	35.00
1873CC	40.00
1873S	35.00

GOLD COINS

DOLLARS: Although gold was coined in the United States from 1795, no dollars were struck until 1849. The initial standard for gold coins in the United States was the $10 piece, the Eagle. The weight of the Eagle was established at 17.496 grams and the fineness at .9166. In 1837 the standards were changed, the weight was made 16.713 grams and the fineness .900. The gold coins of the United States, like those of Canada and Great Britain, have been extensively counterfeited. A collector should be certain of a gold coin's authenticity before purchasing it.

Type 1

Date	Fine
1849	125.00
1849C	150.00
1849D	150.00
1849O	125.00
1850	125.00
1850C	175.00
1850D	150.00
1850O	135.00
1851	125.00
1851C	140.00
1851D	150.00
1851O	125.00
1852	125.00
1852C	150.00
1852D	150.00
1852O	125.00
1853	125.00
1853C	150.00
1853D	175.00
1853O	125.00
1854	125.00
1854D	250.00
1854S	140.00

Type 2

Date	Fine
1854-1855	150.00
1855C	300.00
1855D	900.00

Date	V.G.
1855O	300.00
1856S	250.00

Type 3

Date	Fine
1856D	1,000.00
1856-1857	115.00
1857C	200.00
1857D	300.00
1857S	140.00
1858	115.00
1858D	350.00
1858S	125.00
1859	115.00
1859C	200.00
1859S	125.00
1859D	250.00
1860	105.00
1860D	1,200.00
1860S	125.00
1861	105.00
1862	115.00
1864	175.00
1865	175.00
1866	140.00
1867	150.00
1868	135.00
1869	140.00
1870	140.00
1870S	250.00
1871-1872	150.00
1873-1874	105.00
1875	1,000.00
1876-1877	125.00
1878-1879	140.00
1880	140.00
1881-1889	105.00

2½ DOLLARS (QUARTER EAGLES): Many gold coins were melted down after the Gold Redemption Act of 1933. All United States gold coinage is rare and no issue is legal tender. The Quarter Eagle was authorized April 2, 1792 and the last issue was in 1929.

Capped Bust - Right

Date		Fine
1796	With Stars	3,000.00
1796	No Stars	2,300.00
1797		1,800.00
1798		1,200.00
1802		800.00
1804		1,100.00
1805		700.00
1806	6 over 4	650.00
1806	6 over 5	750.00
1807		600.00

Classic Head

Date	Fine
1834 No Motto	150.00
1835	150.00
1836	150.00
1837-1838	150.00
1838C	200.00
1839	175.00
1839C	175.00
1839D	200.00
1839O	150.00

Capped Head - Left

Date		Fine
1808		2,500.00
1821		750.00
1824		750.00
1825		750.00
1826		1,000.00
1827		750.00
1829-1832		600.00
1833		600.00
1834	With Motto	1,750.00

Coronet Head

Date	Fine
1840-1840O	125.00
1840C	150.00
1840D	200.00
1841C	175.00
1841D	200.00
1842	150.00
1842C	150.00
1842D	175.00
1842O	125.00
1843	125.00

Date	Fine	Date	Fine
1843C & 1843D	150.00	1858C	150.00
1843O	125.00	1859D	225.00
1844	135.00	1859S, 1860	125.00
1844C	150.00	1860C	160.00
1844D	140.00	1860S-1863	125.00
1845	125.00	1864	250.00
1845D	150.00	1865	275.00
1845O	175.00	1865S	125.00
1846-1846O	125.00	1866	140.00
1846C	200.00	1866S	125.00
1846D	150.00	1867	140.00
1847	125.00	1867S-1874	130.00
1847C & 1847D	150.00	1875	800.00
1848	275.00	1875S-1880	125.00
1848C & 1848D	150.00	1877	225.00
1848 CAL over eagle		1881	400.00
Very Rare	1,800.00	1882	135.00
1849	125.00	1883-1884	140.00
1849C & 1849D	140.00	1885	275.00
1850, 1850O, 1851	125.00	1886	140.00
1850C, 1850D, 1851C	140.00	1887, 1890	130.00
1851D	135.00	1888-1889	130.00
1851O, 1852	125.00	1892	140.00
1852C	150.00	1893-1907	125.00
1852D	200.00		
1852O, 1853	125.00		
1853D	250.00		
1854	125.00		
1854C	150.00		
1854D	700.00		
1854O	125.00		
1854S	Very Rare		
1855	125.00		
1855C	300.00		
1855D	1,000.00		
1856, 1856O, 1856S	100.00		
1856C	150.00		
1856D	800.00		
1857D	250.00		
1857O	125.00		
1857-1859	125.00		

Indian Head

Date	Fine
1908-1911	110.00
1911D	250.00
1912-1929	110.00

3 DOLLARS: The $3 gold piece was authorized in February 1853 and first struck in 1854. It was not a popular coin and had a limited circulation as a result.

Date	Fine
1868	325.00
1869	350.00
1870	300.00
1871	350.00
1872	325.00
1873 Proof	Rare
1874	300.00
1877	400.00
1878	250.00
1879	300.00
1880	350.00
1881	450.00
1882	300.00
1883-1884	350.00
1885	375.00
1886	325.00
1887	325.00
1888-1889	325.00

Date	Fine
1854, 1854O	300.00
1854D	1,400.00
1855-1857	300.00
1855S	325.00
1858	325.00
1859-1863	325.00
1864	350.00
1865	350.00
1866	325.00
1867	350.00

4 DOLLARS: There were two designs for these rare patterns. One showed a bust with flowing hair; the other showed a bust with coiled hair. The patterns were struck in four different metals.

Date	Proof
1879	Very Rare
1880	Very Rare

5 DOLLARS (HALF EAGLES): The $5 piece was the first gold coinage minted in the United States. The 1822 issue is regarded as one of the most valuable business strike coins in American currency history. Unlike all other United States coinage, the Half Eagle was struck at all seven mints.

Capped Bust - Right

Date	Fine
1795	1,500.00
1796	1,500.00
1797	2,000.00
1798	500.00
1799	500.00
1800-1807	500.00

Draped Bust - Left

Date	Fine
1807-1812	450.00
1813-1814	450.00
1815	**Rare**
1818	500.00
1819	**Rare**
1820	500.00
1821	1,200.00
1823	800.00
1824	2,500.00
1825	1,200.00
1826	1,500.00
1827	2,500.00
1828	2,000.00
1829	**Rare**
1830	1,200.00
1831	1,200.00
1832	2,000.00
1833	1,200.00
1834 With Motto	1,200.00
1834 No Motto, Plain 4	200.00
1834 No Motto, Crosslet 4	225.00

Classic Head

Date	Fine
1835-1838	200.00
1838C	450.00
1838D	450.00

Coronet Head

Date	Fine
1839	125.00
1839C, 1839D	250.00
1840	125.00
1840C, 1840D	225.00
1840O	135.00
1841	125.00
1841C, 1841D	150.00
1842	125.00
1842O	150.00
1842C, 1842D	175.00
1843	125.00
1843C, 1843D	175.00
1843O	125.00
1844	125.00
1844O	150.00
1844C	200.00
1844D	175.00
1845	125.00
1845O	150.00
1845D	200.00
1846	125.00
1846C, 1846D	200.00
1846O	150.00
1847	125.00
1847C, 1847D, 1847O	175.00
1848	125.00
1848C, 1848D	175.00
1849-1850	125.00
1849C, 1849D	175.00

Date	Fine	Date	Fine
1850C, 1850D	175.00	1869	275.00
1851C, 1851D	175.00	1870	175.00
1851O	150.00	1870S	125.00
1852	125.00	1870CC	700.00
1852C, 1852D	175.00	1871	175.00
1853	125.00	1871S	125.00
1853C, 1853D	175.00	1871CC	225.00
1854	125.00	1872	300.00
1854C, 1854D	175.00	1872S	125.00
1854O	175.00	1872CC	200.00
1854S	Rare	1873	125.00
1855	125.00	1873CC	275.00
1855C, 1855D, 1855O	175.00	1873S	125.00
1855S	125.00	1874	160.00
1856	125.00	1874S	125.00
1856C, 1856D, 1856O	175.00	1874CC	160.00
1856S, 1857	125.00	1875	Rare
1857S	125.00	1875CC	225.00
1857D	175.00	1875S	125.00
1857O, 1857C	175.00	1876	300.00
1858	150.00	1876CC	250.00
1858C, 1858D	175.00	1876S	225.00
1858S	150.00	1877	275.00
1859	125.00	1877S	125.00
1859C, 1859D	175.00	1877CC	200.00
1859S	150.00	1878	125.00
1860	125.00	1878S	125.00
1860C, 1860D	175.00	1878CC	600.00
1860S	140.00	1879, 1879S	125.00
1861	125.00	1879CC	165.00
1861C	600.00	1880, 1880S, 1880CC	125.00
1861S	145.00	1881, 1881S	125.00
1861D	1,800.00	1881CC	135.00
1862	175.00	1882, 1882S, 1882CC	125.00
1862S	150.00	1883, 1883S	125.00
1863	250.00	1883CC	140.00
1863S	140.00	1884, 1884S	125.00
1864	200.00	1884CC	140.00
1864S	600.00	1885, 1886	125.00
1865	250.00	1887S	125.00
1865S	125.00	1888, 1888S	125.00
1866 With Motto	175.00	1889	175.00
1866S With Motto	160.00	1890	200.00
1866S No Motto	140.00	1890CC, 1891CC	125.00
1867-1868	140.00	1891, 1892	125.00
1867S	125.00	1892O	325.00
1868S, 1869S	125.00	1892S, 1892CC	125.00

Date	Fine
1893, 1893S	125.00
1893O	135.00
1893CC	130.00
1894	130.00
1894O	140.00
1895-1904	125.00
1904S	125.00
1905-1908	125.00

Indian Head

Date	Fine
1908-1916	135.00
1929	1,100.00

10 DOLLARS (EAGLE): Many of the early issue gold coins show file marks. These striations, which are also known as adjustment marks, are minting characteristics. The coins with these marks were slightly overweight and were filed to make their weight exact. The rarest issue of Eagles is that of 1798.

Capped Bust - Right

Coronet Head

Date		Fine
1795		1,500.00
1796		1,500.00
1797	Small Eagle	1,500.00
1797	Large Eagle	800.00
1798		1,500.00
1799-1803		800.00
1804		1,000.00

Date	Fine
1838	450.00
1839	350.00
1840, 1841	250.00
1841O	300.00
1842-1857	250.00
1857O	300.00
1857S	250.00
1858O, 1858S	250.00
1859	250.00
1859O	450.00
1859S	300.00

Date	Fine	Date	Fine
1860, 1860O	250.00	1879O	600.00
1860S	300.00	1880, 80S, 80CC, 80O	250.00
1861, 1862	250.00	1881, 81S, 81CC, 81O	250.00
1863	1,200.00	1882, 1882S, 1882O	250.00
1863S	250.00	1882CC	250.00
1864, 1865	350.00	1883, 1883S, 1883CC	250.00
1864S	700.00	1883O	1,100.00
1865S	300.00	1884, 1884S, 1884CC	250.00
1865S No Motto	400.00	1885-1888	250.00
1866 Motto	250.00	1888O, 1888S	250.00
1867	250.00	1889	250.00
1867S	250.00	1889S	250.00
1868, 1868S	250.00	1890, 1890CC	250.00
1869	400.00	1891, 1892	250.00
1869S	250.00	1892CC	250.00
1870	250.00	1892O, 1892S	250.00
1870CC	600.00	1893, 93S, 93O, 93CC	250.00
1870S	250.00	1894-1907	250.00
1871, 1871CC	350.00		
1871S	250.00		
1872	400.00		
1872CC	350.00		
1872S	250.00		
1873	900.00		
1873CC	500.00		
1873S	250.00		
1874	250.00		
1874CC, 1874S	250.00		
1875	Very Rare		
1875CC	300.00		
1876	800.00		
1876CC	350.00		
1876S	250.00		
1877	900.00		
1877CC	450.00		
1877S	250.00		
1878, 1878S	250.00		
1878CC	450.00		
1879, 1879S	250.00		
1879CC	1,100.00		

Indian Head

Date	Fine
1907-1916S	300.00
1920S	2,500.00
1926	300.00
1930S	1,500.00
1932	300.00
1933 None ever in circulation	

$20 DOLLARS (DOUBLE EAGLES): The Double Eagle was the largest denomination coin issued in the United States. It was authorized for coining in 1849. The Saint Gaudens designed issues of 1907-1933 are considered to be among the most attractive coins ever minted in the United States.

Liberty

Date	V.F.
1850	500.00
1850O	500.00
1851	500.00
1851O, 1852O	500.00
1852, 1853, 1853O	500.00
1854, 1854S	500.00
1855, 1855S	500.00
1855O	600.00
1856, 1856S	500.00
1856O	Very Rare
1857, 1857S	500.00
1857O	500.00
1858, 1858S	500.00
1858O	500.00
1859, 1859S	500.00
1859O	800.00
1860, 1860S	500.00
1860O	1,000.00
1861, 1861S	500.00
1861O	750.00
1862, 1862S	500.00
1863, 1863S	500.00
1864, 1864S	500.00
1865, 1865S	500.00
1866 With Motto	500.00
1866S With Motto	500.00

Date	V.F.
1866S No Motto	500.00
1867, 1867S	500.00
1868, 1868S	500.00
1869, 1869S	500.00
1870, 1870S	500.00
1870CC	Very Rare
1871	500.00
1871CC	800.00
1871S	500.00
1872	500.00
1872S	500.00
1872CC	500.00
1873, 1873S	500.00
1873CC	500.00
1874, 1874S, 1874CC	500.00
1875, 1875S, 1875CC	500.00
1876, 1876S, 1876CC	500.00
1877, 1877S, 1877CC	500.00
1878, 1878S	500.00
1878CC	500.00
1879, 1879S	500.00
1879CC	500.00
1879O	1,500.00
1880, 1880S	500.00
1881	1,500.00
1881S	500.00
1882	Rare
1882S, 1882CC	500.00
1883S, 1883CC	500.00
1884S, 1884CC	500.00
1885 Rare	2,000.00
1885CC	500.00
1885S	500.00
1886	2,000.00
1887S	500.00
1888, 1888S	500.00
1889, 1889S, 1889CC	500.00
1890, 1890S, 1890CC	500.00
1891	1,000.00
1891CC	600.00
1891S	500.00
1892	900.00
1892CC	500.00
1892S	500.00
1893, 1893S	500.00
1893CC	500.00
1894-1907	500.00

St. Gaudens

Date	V.F.
1907-1913	400.00
1909D	450.00
1913S	425.00
1914-1920	400.00
1920S	2,500.00

Date	Fine
1921	2,500.00
1922, 1922S	400.00
1923, 1923D	400.00
1924	400.00
1924D, 1924S	500.00
1925D	500.00
1925S	400.00
1926	400.00
1926D	600.00
1926S	425.00
1927	400.00
1927D	Very Rare
1927S	1,500.00
1928	400.00
1929	1,500.00
1930S	3,000.00
1931	2,000.00
1931D	2,500.00
1932	2,500.00

GOLD COMMEMORATIVE COINS

Date and Denomination			E.F.
1903	$1.00	Louisiana Purchase, Jefferson	150.00
1903	$1.00	Louisiana Purchase, McKinley	150.00
1904	$1.00	Louis & Clark Exposition	300.00
1905	$1.00	Louis & Clark Exposition	300.00
1915S	$1.00	Panama-Pacific Exposition	100.00
1916	$1.00	McKinley Memorial	100.00
1917	$1.00	McKinley Memorial	100.00
1922	$1.00	Grant Memorial, with star	250.00
1922	$1.00	Grant Memorial, without star	250.00
1915S	$2.50	Panama-Pacific Exposition	350.00
1926	$2.50	Philadelphia Sesquicentennial	110.00

COINS OF GREAT BRITAIN

COPPER COINS

Charles II (1660-1684)	V.G.
Farthing 1672-75, 79	2.25
Halfpenny 1672, 73, 75	3.25

William III (1694-1702)	V.G.
Farthing 1695-1700	2.75
Halfpenny 1695-1701	2.75

James II (1685-1688)	V.G.
Farthing (tin) 1684-87	35.00
Halfpenny (tin) 1685-87	35.00

Anne (1702-1714)	V.G.
Farthing 1714	30.00

William & Mary (1688-1694)	V.G.
Farthing (tin) 1689, 90, 92	40.00
Halfpenny (tin)	40.00
Farthing (copper) 1694	1.75
Halfpenny (copper) 1694	2.75

George I (1714-1727)	V.G.
Farthing	1.75
Halfpenny	1.75

George II (1727-1760)	V.G.
Farthing	1.75
Halfpenny	1.75

GEORGE III: In the early 1770's copper farthings were struck in the name of George III, and when these issues were finished no new coins were released for some 20 years. Between 1770 and 1800 there was so much counterfeiting in England that most of the heavy, authorized coinage was quickly melted down and recast as lightweight imitation. Matthew Boulton proposed a solution based on intrinsic value coinage. His designs known as the cartwheel penny and twopence proposed that a penny would weigh one ounce avoirdupois (28.34 grams) which would give it an intrinsic value similar to its face value. These issues were authorized in 1797 and were coined until 1807.

George III (1760-1820)	V.G.		
		Penny 1806-07	.75
Farthing	.75	Penny (cartwheel) 1797	1.75
Halfpenny	1.00	Twopence (cartwheel) 1797	2.75

GEORGE IV: Only farthings were issued in the first five years of the reign. The initial obverse design by B. Pistrucci was not liked and in 1826 a design by William Wyon was implemented.

George IV (1820-1830)	V.G.
Third Farthing (for Malta)	1.00
Half Farthing (for Ceylon)	2.00
Farthing	2.25
Halfpenny	2.00
Penny	3.00

WILLIAM IV: The fractional farthings issued in different reigns were intended solely for colonies that used English currency. The third farthing in both copper and bronze was for use in Malta, and the copper quarter and half farthing were for use in Ceylon. In 1842 the half farthing was made current in England, and it remained so until copper currency was discontinued in 1862. The designs for the William IV coinage were by Sir Francis Chantrey.

William IV (1830-1837)	V.G.
Third Farthing 1835 (for Malta)	1.25
Half Farthing 1837 (for Ceylon)	1.50
Farthing	.75
Halfpenny	1.25
Penny	2.25

VICTORIA: The "Young Head" design was by William Wyon. In the "Young Head" copper issues of penny and halfpenny there were a number of altered dates resulting from overcutting dies of previous years.

In 1860 a shift was made to bronze coinage. Since the earlier copper coinage did not wear well a new mixture of 95% copper and 5% zinc and tin was introduced. During the 1870's and 1880's much of the bronze coinage was struck at the Heaton Mint in Birmingham, and shows a small "H" under the date as a mint mark.

The "Veiled Head" issues were engraved by G. DeSaulles from designs by Thomas Brock for the obverse and William Wyon for the reverse. Most of the 1897 farthings, and all those of the following years up to 1917 were given a dark finish. In 1918 a bright finish was re-instituted.

Young Head Issues

Large Size - Copper

Victoria (1837-1901)	V.G.
Quarter Farthing 1839-53 (for Ceylon)	2.50
Third Farthing 1844 (for Malta)	2.00
Half Farthing 1839-56	.50
Farthing 1838-60	.50
Halfpenny 1838-60	1.00
Penny 1839-60	2.25

Farthing	V.G.
1860	.30
1861	.30
1862	.30
1863	4.50
1864	.25
1865	.25
1866-68	.25
1869	.75
1872	.70
1873-74H	.75
1875	3.50
1875H	1.00
1876H	2.00
1878-79	1.00
1880	1.00
1881	1.00
1881H-83	.30
1884-86	.20
1887-88	.20
1890	.20
1891	.20
1892	.50
1893	.20
1894	.20
1895	2.50

Small Size - Bronze

Third Farthing	V.G.
1866-85 (for Malta)	.50

Halfpenny	V.G.
1860-61	.30
1862	.30
1863	.35
1864	.80
1865	.75
1866	.60
1867	1.00
1868	1.00
1869	1.25
1870	1.50
1871	4.00
1872	1.00
1873	1.00
1874	2.00
1874H	.75
1875	.60
1875H	2.00
1876H	.50

Penny	V.G.
1877	.50
1878	1.25
1879	.50
1880-81	.60
1881H	.50
1882H	.50
1883	.50
1884	.45
1885-94	.35

Penny	V.G.
1879	.50
1880	.75
1881	.75
1881H	.70
1882H-84	.35
1885-93	.35
1894	.35

Veiled Head Issues

Penny	V.G.
1860-61	.75
1862-63	.75
1864	2.00
1865	1.00
1866	1.00
1867	.75
1868	.75
1869	14.00
1870	2.00
1871	1.75
1872	1.75
1873	.65
1874	.65
1874H	.65
1875	.65
1875H	3.50
1876H-77	.65
1878	1.00

Farthing	V.G.
1895-1897	.10
1898	.15
1899-1901	.15

Halfpenny	V.G.
1895	.30
1896-1897	.30
1898	.20
1899-1901	.20

Penny	V.G.
1895	.30
1896-1900	.25
1901	.10

EDWARD VII: The coinage of Edward VII which was first issued in 1902 used an obverse designed by G. DeSaulles and the same reverse as the late Victorian pieces only with some minor alterations.

Farthing	V.G.
1902-1909	.10
1910	.30

Halfpenny	V.G.
1902-1910	.10

Edward VII (1902-1910)   V.G.

Third Farthing 1902 (for Malta)   .75

Penny	V.G.
1902-1910	.10

GEORGE V: Considerable difficulty was encountered in the initial strikings of the coinage. The halfpenny used a high relief portrait which caused a metal displacement that resulted in an outline of the head showing on the reverse. A new alloy was used in 1923 which was softer and reduced the problem somewhat while giving longer die life as well. However it was not until a new, smaller portrait was introduced in 1928 that the "ghosting" problem was completely corrected.

In 1912, 1918, and 1919 the Heaton Mint struck pennies which are identified with an "H" mint mark. In the latter two of those years the Kings Norton Metal Co., Ltd. (K.N. mint mark) also struck coins.

The 1933 issues were not released except for some ceremonial specimens.

Farthing	Fine
1911-1933	.05
1934	.15
1935	1.50
1936	.10

Halfpenny	Fine
1911-1924	.40
1925-1928	.25
1929-1934	.10
1935	.15
1936	.15

George V (1911-1936)   V.G.

Third Farthing 1913 (for Malta)   .75

Penny	Fine	Penny	V.G.
1911-1912	.15		
1912H	.15	1919H	.35
1913-1918	.10	1919KN	1.40
1918H	.35	1920-1922	.10
1918KN	1.00	1926	.15
1919	.20	1927-1936	.05

GEORGE VI: A new style of reverse design was introduced in 1937 with the Wren reverse for the farthing and The Golden Hind reverse for the halfpenny. The farthing was minted with the Wren reverse until 1956 when production of that denomination was stopped. On January 1, 1961 it was announced that the farthing was discontinued as a valid currency.

The penny was minted intermittently during the reign of George VI. No new coins were needed from 1941 to 1943, and in 1949 minting stopped, for the most part, for a number of years. There were some 1950 and 1951 pennies struck, but these were primarily for specimen sets.

George VI (1937-1951)	Fine
Farthing 1937-1952	.05
Halfpenny 1937-1945	.05
Halfpenny 1946	.15
Halfpenny 1947	.07
Halfpenny 1948	.05
Halfpenny 1949	.07
Halfpenny 1950-1952	.05
Penny 1937-1946	.03
Penny 1947-1949	.04
Penny 1950	2.50
Penny 1951	4.00

ELIZABETH II: The 1953 halfpenny with an obverse design by Mary Gillick had a low relief and later in the year the dies were retouched to make the details sharper. In 1954 all the coinage dropped the "BRITT: OMM:" from the Royal titles.

Elizabeth II (1953 to date)	E.F.
Farthing 1953-1955	.03
Farthing 1956	.25
Halfpenny 1953	.15
Halfpenny 1954-1960	.03
Penny 1953	.75
Penny 1961	.10

GOLD COINS
Sovereigns

The first sovereigns were produced in 1817. The Victorian issues appeared with a number of different designs. The "Young Head" issue had both a shield and a St. George pattern reverse. There were also the Jubilee issue of 1887 and the "Veiled Head" issues which began in 1893.

The George V sovereigns were struck each year from 1911 to 1917, but it is unlikely that any were released for circulation after 1915. The issue of 1925 was not for circulation but strictly for the Bank of England's gold reserve. Numbers of sovereigns were struck in 1949, 1951, and 1952 with a 1925 date. These coins were circulated among banks in order to make the sovereign a current coin. This would make private strikings of the denomination in other countries in violation of counterfeit laws.

Sovereigns:
Victoria, Edward VII, George V, Elizabeth II 55.00

Half-Sovereigns

On the reverse of the Victorian issues of 1863 to 1880 there was a small die number. This number was used by the mint to establish the life of an individual die. In 1881 and 1882 there were no issues of half-sovereigns because the mint was being rebuilt. Half-sovereigns of the Victorian era were also minted in Australia, in Sydney from 1855 and Melbourne from 1872.

The George V half-sovereigns were only coined at the English mint for the first five years of the reign; however, the Australian and South African mints continued production as late as 1926. For George VI and Elizabeth II the gold coins were only struck for coronation sets.

Half-sovereigns:
Victoria, Edward VII, George V 45.00

Two Pounds and Five Pounds

Two Pounds 175.00
Five Pounds 350.00

APPENDIX -- BULLION VALUES

Silver and gold coins and other numismatic items are often bought by dealers for their bullion value, that is the value of the pure precious metals which they contain. The weight of precious metals is expressed in grams or troy ounces, not in avoirdupois ounces. A troy ounce is greater than an avoirdupois ounce:

$$1 \text{ Troy Ounce} = 31.103 \text{ Grams}$$
$$1 \text{ Avoirdupois Ounce} = 28.349 \text{ Grams}$$

GOLD

The quantity of pure gold in gold coins is calculated by multiplying the gold fineness or purity of the coin by its weight in troy ounces or grams. Gold purity can also be expressed in karats, a 24-part system with 24 karats equalling pure gold, 22 karats equalling 22 parts gold to 2 parts base metal, 18 karats equalling 18 parts gold to 6 parts base metal etc.

Karats	Fineness	Purity
24	.999	99.9%
22	.916	91.6%
18	.750	75.0%
14	.585	58.5%
10	.417	41.7%
9	.375	37.5%

A 14-karat or .585 fine gold coin weighing 1 troy ounce contains 1 ounce × .585 = .585 troy ounces of pure gold. If gold is worth $600 per troy ounce, then this coin is worth $600 × .585 = $351. (See extended charts on following pages.)

SILVER

The quantity of pure silver in silver coins is calculated by multiplying the silver fineness or purity of the coin by its weight in troy ounces or grams.

Standard	Fineness	Purity
Pure	.999	99.9%
Fine	.999	99.9%
Sterling	.925	92.5%
Coin	.800	80.0%
Coin	.500	50.0%

A .800 fine silver coin weighing 1 troy ounce contains 1 ounce × .800 = .800 troy ounces of pure silver. If silver is worth $20 an ounce, then this coin is worth $20 × .800 = $16. (See extended charts on following pages.)

GOLD CONTENT OF CANADIAN GOLD COINS

Denom.	Date and Mint Mark	Gross Weight (Grams)	Fineness	Pure Gold Content (Grams)	(Troy Oz.)
NEWFOUNDLAND					
$2	1865-1888	3.33	.917	3.05	.100
CANADA					
£1	1908C-1910C	7.99	.917	7.32	.236
£1	1911C-1919C	7.99	.917	7.32	.236
$5	1912-1914	8.36	.900	7.52	.242
$10	1912-1914	16.72	.900	15.05	.484
$20	1967	18.27	.900	16.45	.529
$50	1979-1980	31.10	.999	31.10	1.000
$100	1976 (Unc.)	13.33	.583	7.78	.250
$100	1976 (Proof)	16.96	.917	15.55	.499
$100	1977	16.96	.917	15.55	.499
$100	1979	16.96	.917	15.55	.499
$100	1980	16.96	.917	15.55	.499

BULLION VALUES OF CANADIAN GOLD COINS

(Computed from $400/troy ounce to $1,000/troy ounce in increments of $100 Canadian)

Denom.	Date & Mint Mark	$400	$500	$600	$700	$800	$900	$1,000
NEWFOUNDLAND								
$2	1865-1888	40.00	50.00	60.00	70.00	80.00	90.00	100.00
CANADA								
*1	1908C-1910C	94.40	118.00	141.60	165.20	188.80	212.40	236.00
*1	1911C-1919C	94.40	118.00	141.60	165.20	188.80	212.40	236.00
$5	1912-1914	96.80	121.00	145.20	169.40	193.60	217.80	242.00
$10	1912-1914	193.60	242.00	290.40	338.80	387.20	435.60	484.00
$20	1967	211.60	264.50	317.40	370.30	423.20	476.10	529.00
$50	1979-1908	400.00	500.00	600.00	700.00	800.00	900.00	1,000.00
$100	1976 (Unc.)	100.00	125.00	150.00	175.00	200.00	225.00	250.00
$100	1976 (Proof)	199.60	249.50	299.40	349.30	399.20	449.10	499.00
$100	1977	199.60	249.50	299.40	349.30	399.20	449.10	499.00
$100	1979	199.60	249.50	299.40	349.30	399.20	449.10	499.00
$100	1980	199.60	249.50	299.40	349.30	399.20	449.10	499.00

SILVER CONTENT OF CANADIAN SILVER COINS

Denom.	Date	Fineness	Silver Content (Grams)	Silver Content (Troy Oz.)
$1	1935 - 1967	.800	18.661	.600
$1	1971 - date	.500	11.662	.375
50¢	1870 - 1919	.925	10.792	.347
50¢	1920 - 1967	.800	9.330	.300
25¢	1870 - 1919	.925	5.370	.173
25¢	1920 - 1967	.800	4.665	.150
25¢	1967 - 1968	.500	2.923	.094
10¢	1858 - 1919	.925	2.146	.069
10¢	1920 - 1967	.800	1.866	.060
10¢	1967 - 1968	.500	1.170	.038
5¢	1858 - 1919	.925	1.080	.034
5¢	1920 - 1921	.800	.933	.030

BULLION VALUES OF CANADIAN SILVER COINS

(Computed from $10/troy ounce to $70/troy ounce in increments of $10 Canadian)

Denom.	Fineness	$10	$20	$30	$40	$50	$60	$70
$1	.800	6.00	12.00	18.00	24.00	30.00	36.00	42.00
$1	.500	3.75	7.50	11.25	15.00	18.75	22.50	26.25
50¢	.925	3.47	6.94	10.41	13.88	17.35	20.82	24.29
50¢	.800	3.00	6.00	9.00	12.00	15.00	18.00	21.00
25¢	.925	1.73	3.46	5.19	6.92	8.65	10.38	12.11
25¢	.800	1.50	3.00	4.50	6.00	7.50	9.00	10.50
25¢	.500	.94	1.88	2.82	3.76	4.70	5.64	6.58
10¢	.925	.69	1.38	2.07	2.76	3.45	4.14	4.83
10¢	.800	.60	1.20	1.80	2.40	3.00	3.60	4.20
10¢	.500	.38	.76	1.14	1.52	1.90	2.28	2.66
5¢	.925	.34	.68	1.02	1.36	1.70	2.04	2.38
5¢	.800	.30	.60	.90	1.20	1.50	1.80	2.10

GLOSSARY

ASSAY: Analytical test to determine the purity and weight of metal.

BAG MARKS: Slight scratches and nicks acquired by coins in contact with others in a mint bag. Most common on large and heavy silver and gold coins.

BLANKS: Flat, round metal discs or planchets from which the coins are made.

BROCKAGE: A coin with the same design raised on one side and incuse on the other, caused by a previously struck coin sticking in the die and striking another blank.

BULLION: Uncoined gold or silver in the form of bars, ingots and plates. Bullion value is a term used in reference to value of metal content in common and mutilated gold and silver coins.

BUSINESS STRIKE: Any coin struck with the intention of circulating as money.

CABINET FRICTION: The friction on uncirculated coins attributed to their storage in a collection.

CAMEO-EFFECT: A description of the appearance of certain gold and silver proof coins which have frosty devices on highly polished fields.

CARAT: The degree of fineness of gold. Pure gold is 24 carats and most gold coins have a fineness of 22 carats.

CLASHED DIES: Damaged dies caused by the absence of a planchet at the time of striking. Each die retains a portion of its opposite's design, in addition to its own. The resulting coins show a partial impression of the reverse design on the obverse and/or vice versa. Such marks will be referred to as clash marks.

CLEANED: A general term referring to cleaning a coin by any method. This often reduces the value and is not recommended.

COIN: A piece of metal with a distinctive design, a fixed value, a specific weight and diameter, which was issued by a government as money.

COLLAR: The part of the die which affixes to the edge of the planchet to prevent movement during striking. Reeded edge coins are made by having the collar grooved; 12 sided five-cent pieces are made by having regular round blanks struck in a 12 sided collar.

COMMEMORATIVE: A coin issued to commemorate a special event or honour an outstanding person.

DEBASEMENT: Debasement of a coin takes place when the issuing authority reduces the purity of the metal, lowering the intrinsic value of the coin but circulating it at par with the previous coins of the original purity. This happened in Canada in 1968 when the silver content of coins for circulation was replaced entirely with nickel.

DENTICLES: The device used around the periphery of a coin to discourage counterfeiters.

DEVICE: Any design feature appearing on the obverse, reverse or edge of a coin.

DIADEMED: A coin where the portrait head has a headband or fillet as a sign of royalty.

DIE: Engraved metal pieces used to impress the design of a coin on a blank planchet.

DIE BULGE: A roundish, raised area on a coin caused by the swelling of a die.

DIE CRACK: A raised line appearing on a coin reflecting a stress crack which developed on the die.

DIE STRIATION: A series of fine, raised and nearly parallel lines resulting from extreme pressure used in the striking of a coin. Occasionally seen on well struck gem business strikes.

ESSAI: A trial piece from dies already accepted for regular coinage. It may bear a date or mint mark other than on the coins issued for circulation or it may be a different metal.

EXERGUE: The lower part of a coin or medal which is usually divided from the "field" by a line under which is contained the date, place of minting or engraver's initials.

FIELD: The open areas on either side of a coin not occupied by the portrait, design or inscription.

FIRST-STRIKE: A coin struck from new dies. Usually fully struck and frequently proof-like.

FLAN: The blank metal cut to shape but before receiving the die impression. Also called a planchet.

HIGH POINTS: The highest points on the design of a coin. The first points to show wear.

IMPAIRED PROOF: A coin struck as a proof but no longer in mint state.

INCUSE: Coins with either obverse or reverse design sunk below the coin's surface. A design raised above the surface is in relief.

INGOT: A piece of precious metal shaped in a mould. Much of the gold reserves of various nations are stored in ingots and bars.

INTRINSIC: The intrinsic value of a coin is the actual metal value of the coin. Canadian silver coins before 1968 are worth more intrinsically than the face value, while the nickel 10¢, 25¢, 50¢ and $1 coin from 1968 to date are worth less intrinsically than the face value.

IRIDESCENT: A multi-coloured blending or toning, frequently found in older uncirculated coins.

LEGEND: The principal inscription on a coin.

MATTE PROOF: A proof coin for which the planchet is treated in a manner other than polishing. A dull and grainy finish is achieved.

MEDAL: A commemorative metal piece in honour of a person or event. Not money.

MINT ERROR: A misstruck or defective coin produced by a mint.

MINT MARK: Letter designation for a branch mint product.

MULE: A coin struck from dies not designed to be used together.

OBVERSE: The "face-up" side of the coin, regarded as more important than the reverse side and usually bearing the portrait of the monarch.

OVERDATE: The date made by an engraver at the mint punching one or more numbers on a previously dated die.

OVERSTRIKE: A coin where part of the design, particularly the date, appears under another design or date.

PATINA: A green or brown surface film frequently found on ancient copper and bronze coins caused by oxidation over a long period of time. Also by moisture and certain soils.

PATTERN: A submitted design sample by engravers when a new coinage is contemplated. If the design is adopted for regular coinage with the same date, the piece ceases to be a pattern.

PLANCHET: The metal disc from which a coin is made. Also called a flan.

PLANCHET DEFECT: The general terms for any of several types of imperfections on a planchet.

PLANCHET FLAKE: A geometrically shaped depressed area of a coin which occurred in preparation of the planchet.

PRESENTATION PIECE: A coin which was struck for a purpose other than to circulate or to sell to the public; similar to a proof.

PROOF: The highest quality of coins struck for collectors and using specially polished or otherwise prepared dies.

PROOF-LIKE: An uncirculated coin having received special minting treatment and a mirror surface for the benefit of collectors with minor imperfections due to the minting process permissable.

REEDING: The graining or milling which appears on the edges of many coins.

RELIEF: A relief design is one where the lettering and design is raised above the surface of the coin. The opposite of incuse.

RESTRIKE: Any coin struck later than the date appearing on the coin.

REVERSE: Opposite from obverse. The back or "tails" side of a coin.

ROTATED DIE: Dies are positioned and locked on a coining press by means of a key. When these keys come loose, rotation can occur resulting in the next coin being struck with the obverse and reverse dies rotated. Coins struck from rotated dies are errors.

SPECIMEN: A general term applying to any specially produced collectors' coin.

TOKEN: Usually a piece of durable material unofficially issued for monetary, advertising, services or other purposes.

TRIAL PIECE: A piece struck at any stage in the preparation of regular dies up to the point of their being put to use for the striking of actual coins.

TYPE: A coin's basic distinguishing design.

UNCIRCULATED: A piece in new condition as issued by a mint.

VARIETY: Any alteration in the basic design of a coin. A major variety is a coin of the same date, mint mark and denomination as another, but struck from another pair of dies and having at least the major device added, removed or redesigned. A minor variety is easily recognizable from the other, though all major devices are similar.

Literature

If you are interested in further information about Canadian currency, then you should consult The Charlton Standard Catalogue of Canadian Coins and The Charlton Standard Catalogue of Canadian Paper Money. The Charlton Standard Catalogue of Canadian Tokens is forthcoming.

Publications of interest to collectors of Canadian currencies are also available from:

The Canadian Numismatic Association,
P.O. Box 226,
Barrie, Ontario.
L4M 4T2
(The C.N.A. publishes The Canadian Numismatic Journal)

The American Numismatic Association,
P.O. Box 2366,
Colorado Springs, Colorado. 80901
(The A.N.A. publishes The Numismatist)